What people are saying abo

These amazing stories from Fran Lewis — will captivate and haunt you long after you turn the last page. Lewis is a unique storyteller who opens the supernatural door for us to hear the dead tell their spellbinding tales and reveal their secrets. An unforgettable read!

R.G. Belsky
author of the Clare Carlson mystery series

Accused is eerily captivating ... thought provoking... a warning. The stories convey a dark, eye-opening theme—pay attention!

Fran Lewis dives into timeless issues with an almost gothic-style of story-telling that will keep you reading and feeling every story as it unfolds. Fran sends a message in her stories. Can you feel it?

TJ O'Connor
award-winning author of *The Hemingway Deception*

Once again Ms. Lewis has a hit with *Accusations,* the fifth book her Faces Behind the Stones series. It's a surefire hit!

This is the most chilling of her books to date!!!

Karen Vaughan
Author of *Dead to Writes*

Silent Voices speak from the grave in this gothic style collection of short stories by Fran Lewis.

If you ever felt wronged and thought of revenge, one of these characters in *Accused* could do the job for you and do it well. And you might find you agree with me that some of the characters deserve what they get.

The atmosphere and characters feel real in these stories and you are drawn in to see what happens next. At times I was there with them in their GRAVES. I read the whole book in two short sittings.

Fran Lewis is one of my go-to authors for great short stories. As a short story writer and reader myself, I was fascinated by the fabulous imagery in this collection.

You will be enthralled by Fran Lewis' talent. "The Grandmother" is my favorite. This grandmother outwits her three granddaughters and they don't see it coming.

You can find more stories like these in Fran's other books; *Faces Behind the Stones, Bad Choices* and *Hidden Truths & Lies*. Enjoy this read!

Jan Holiday

Accusations

FRAN LEWIS

ISBN: 978-1-955622-30-1

Dedications

I also want to dedicate this book to my grandmother, Katie Goldberg, who shared her story with me, and my Grandmother Bertha, who I really never got to know.

I also want to thank my cousins Hedy Braverman, Stacy Modlin, and Eunice Pasher for their input on the story titled Bertha.

A big thank-you to my friend Marilyn, who gave me the title for this book, Accusations, and ideas for the stories.

I also want to thank my nephew Josh, who supports all of my writing, endeavors, and more.

These stories might be fiction, but the first two are based on real life situations.

Contents

PART 1

Faces:
What Voices Lie
Behind the Stones?

Driving down the rocky path, I saw the overgrown grass, weeds, and poison ivy overtaking the outer perimeter of the bushes. The smell of mildew, of the dried bones of animals coming up from the ground killed by cars along this dirt road, the sadness on the faces of the drivers in the cars behind us — I could feel their pain and sorrow.

I began to wonder what they were thinking, what their thoughts and feelings were as they travelled down life's highway, possibly for the very last time. What stories lie hidden among the faces behind those wheels of each car? Faces ... so, so many stories. Here are seven that will make chills run down your spine as you wonder: What lies behind the stones? Who lives there? ...

My next stop is a huge marble headstone with the name Virginia on it. Her date of birth has not been placed on the stone, nor has her date of death. She is somewhere behind this stone all alone, and her voice must be heard. How did she become the next face behind the stone? I can hear her voice loud and clear as the driver comes to a stop in front of her stone and some get out to pay their final respects.

What follows is an unauthorized account of what happens when someone is sent to await his or her fate in the Rubber Room. Meet Virginia Green...

THE ACCUSED:

Virginia Green

The Voice Behind the Second Stone,
Listen and hope this does not happen to you!

Prologue

My life is not comprised of colors, or people, or things; it is comprised of many different shapes that form my personality. Sometimes, I feel like I live within a square wall with all four sides tightly shut and no way to escape. Sometimes, I feel like I am in the center of a circle that has no beginning and no end, as I go 'round and 'round but get nowhere. At times, my life resembles a triangle — a scalene triangle — with unequal sides and angles, which comprises my three different personalities, often in conflict with each other.

These are my stories. Each one tells what happens when I drift into one of my shapes, feel alone, and then disappear

1

into my own world. I am all of these people, and somewhere, I don't know where, I can be found.

I cannot deal with my life anymore. It is time to end the pain. Look at the rainbows in these bottles and all their pretty colors, which I can take to ease my mind, clear my head, and rest without the throbbing pain in my head, arms, and shoulders. I go through life in a fog that never seems to lift, with a huge cumulonimbus cloud hanging over me, just before the thunder and lightning strike and the whole world explodes into one horrific bolt of darkness. There are red, blue, green, yellow, and purple ones in this bottle. I think I will take one of each. After all, they all work the same way, and they help me deal with life, subduing the pain and sorrow I endure as I float into oblivion and drift slowly to a better place and time.

There are many reasons that people feel as if their lives are going nowhere and somehow, they do not matter. Many even feel that when they are in a room, no one sees them, even though they exist in plain sight. But what happens when you feel that your whole life is about to take a turn for the worse, and there is nothing you can do about it? That you are about to disappear — not in a physical sense — but into your own mind, a world of your own. It is a world so terrifying that you cannot control your actions, your words, or even your environment. Before I end it all, I want you to hear my voice and read my story. To see what happens when you are wrongly accused and no one cares!

Before the end, let me tell you the beginning...

I have spent months in this room, collecting full pay and feeling worthless; not allowed to perform any duties, not even clerical work. I spend my time daydreaming, thinking of my life before this happened, and hoping that someday I will wake up, and it will all have been a bad dream. Along with the others in this room, I feel unwanted, dejected, and without self-worth. Sitting here in silence, living on the edge and feeling hopeless, I realize that prisoners in jail have more freedoms and rights than we do, and we have not even been formally charged. The charges against me cannot be proven. I would never injure a child, and I am far from incompetent.

What is worse is that none of my so-called friends will even speak to me or return my calls. These are the same people who needed my help and guidance when they first started teaching. There is a general consensus among all of the inmates in this living prison: we are tarnished and diseased and not worth being near. Even those that have been acquitted still have the stigma of being wrongly accused and have to work hard to regain the respect and trust of other teachers. People with AIDS, tuberculosis, and other contagious diseases get better treatment than us.

Throughout the city school system every year, many teachers, principals, guidance counselors, and school custodians have been accused of many types of infractions. Some for abuse of some type on a student, teacher, or administrator; some for being insubordinate. No matter what these people are accused of, they are considered guilty in the eyes of the media, the public, and their colleagues, whether they are or not. Removed from their positions, many are placed in situations that become untenable. Administrators are placed on administrative duties, but teachers and guidance counselors are placed in what the system has so aptly deemed **The Rubber Room.** Although the walls might not be made of actual rubber, the environment is conducive to that of a prison cell without the bars.

This is a room where hundreds of NYC schoolteachers are sitting, paid full salary and forced to do absolutely nothing. Deemed guilty as charged even before an investigation is underway, they are suspended from their positions, and their teaching assignments are temporarily gone but indefinitely revoked. Barred, banned, and no longer allowed near students, classrooms, or schools, they sit in an off-campus location, waiting.

Teachers are assigned to this room and spend many months, if not years, waiting for their cases to be heard, hoping to finally be allowed to return to teaching. Sitting idly by each day, they receive full salaries for doing nothing. How redeeming is that?

With budget cuts, overcrowded classrooms, and schools complaining about the lack of books, supplies, and money for afterschool programs, these educators, who might not be guilty, are rotting away in these horrific rooms simply because, as in my case, they were wrongly accused.

How It All Began

My life is hell at this very moment. I had a great career, a great family, and some pretty nice friends. But, when adversity strikes and you are put in the hot seat, everyone turns a blind eye — or in this case, a cold one — when you need them. From having great friends whom I would commiserate with at work to having a polar ice cap thrown in my direction, my life has turned into a living nightmare all because of one person.

You would think that this person had some knowledge of what we do as educators. She does not. She pushes her pen back and forth on paper daily, attempting to sign her name on documents but in reality, she needs others to guide her, or things would be even worse. Never having modeled a lesson or really taught anyone anything, she observes us teachers not with a critical eye to help us and guide us but rather in order to cripple our spirits, to destroy our self-esteem and obliterate us from the educational system as people.

We become the victims because this person feels that, after decades of service, we are no longer useful. We are the ones who have opinions, speak up for injustices, and never cower to her demands. We are the ones who really care about the students, and not only can we discipline them and have control but also teach them successfully. Here is my story. My voice needs to be heard to prevent this from happening to others.

How I Got Here

I have no idea how I got here or why things got so out of hand that I wound up in this miserable place with all of these losers ... well, I guess they consider me to be one of them, too. I am not! I sit here, facing these poor excuses for humans, staring at their blank faces while I ponder my future and decide if life is still worth living. How did I get here? Let's start from the beginning.

About a month ago, as I was entering the main office of my school, two male security guards blocked my way and told me to wait in the outer hall. They did not say why when I asked them. I was not about to take their abuse and harassment or be embarrassed. So, I tried skirting around them, when one of them took hold of my arm; at that point, I threatened to call the police. Backing off, they told me that the principal did not want me entering the office and that she would be right out.

As usual, this wicked excuse for an administrator sauntered out about twenty minutes later, ordering me into her office through the back door. She said nothing, and her facial expression was stone cold, yet I saw a glint in her eyes: I could tell she was really enjoying herself.

There were five people in her office. Realizing that they were not school personnel but police officers, I immediately called my husband for help. I knew that I needed a lawyer but had no idea why.

One of the men approached me and said that I was accused of drinking hard liquor during my breaks and coming back from lunch drunk. I was also accused of hitting several students in my second-grade class. Now, I knew that they were nuts. I never hit my kids, and I rarely raise my voice to my students; why, in heaven's name, would I do such a horrible thing? Even worse, I was not given a chance to explain. Taken out of the school, my personal things placed in a cardboard box, I felt humiliated and embarrassed. They escorted me out in front of the students and parents in the school lobby.

In some schools, these incidents are not always reported. However, this principal reported everything and ratted on everyone, even if she knew they were not guilty. She enjoyed the limelight and would stop at nothing to humiliate a staff member. She considered teachers as just pawns that worked for her. Unfortunately, she could be very intimidating, and no one ever spoke up. Most of the seasoned teachers that had been in the school for over twenty-five years either transferred, retired, or started new careers. The fact that she was still there was both mindboggling and horrific.

You would think that a person would be innocent until proven guilty, not in this case. I was a talented, well-respected educator with an impeccable reputation in a school in the Bronx. I was involved with the union and served as chapter chairman for a while. But she told the authorities I was a drunk, a child abuser, and worse.

These heinous charges against me were invented to force me to retire or remove me from the school; this would show everyone that she was in charge, that she would do anything in her power to humiliate someone who did not cower to her every wish. Being accused of corporal punishment is unthinkable. Yelling at me in front of the parents, the police, and the investigative team, she threatened to publicize this information if I dared to speak up.

I told her to go right ahead and let the lawsuits begin. But, truthfully, I was starting to get scared and felt sick to my stomach. I did not know how much more I could take — and it was just the beginning.

I was taken to the district office and placed in a room by myself until someone came to question me. With no legal representation, I was not willing to speak to anyone, so I just sat there not knowing what to do. Calling my chapter leader so she could notify the union, I hoped they would send someone that would be of help to me — not so. Administrators have too much power and they often abuse it, as she did. She never followed procedure, she never gave me a chance to explain; she only acted upon information provided to her by a child with a discipline problem, her two friends willing to lie for her, and a teacher who was in her hip pocket and who I thought was my friend but was not.

Wrongly accused and heartbroken, I was deemed guilty before I could speak in my defense. Here is what happens when you are placed in what we call the Rubber Room. Here is what your daily fate is.

I was assigned to a single room in Barnesville High School, just like many others in the same situation.

Here I Am: Rubber Room Resident and Worse!

I guess I was not the only one in my school to receive this special treatment. Teachers are not only sent to the Rubber Room for committing abuse or other physical infractions but some who are deemed incompetent are re-condemned. Such is the plight of me, Virginia Green, a second-grade teacher who has been reduced to a shadow of myself since learning that I can no longer teach my precious students. It seems that the powers that should not oversee the school, the ones who spend too much time locked in their offices drinking coffee and having meetings, decided, after many observations, that I should receive a U, or unsatisfactory, rating; and not just one, but three consecutive U's. No one tried to help me or give me any aid. They decided that, after over twenty years of teaching, I was expendable. After receiving the last "U," I went to my chapter leader to ask what my next step should be, but as she was new to the position, she was of little to no help.

As I think back to that fateful day, I remember receiving a termination letter from my principal. As I stated, I immediately went to the chapter chairman for help and was told to contact the union directly. After explaining my problem to a union representative, I was assigned a lawyer to assist me with the appeal. Filling out the form that explained the charges brought against me, I started to cry. What is worse, they require you to prove the allegations on your own. How was I supposed to prove that I was competent if the principal said I was and had put it in writing?

Well, Virginia, start thinking. I wrote down that not until she became principal did I ever have a poor rating, and that is something I could prove. I had letters from past principals who praised me, plus one year I was honored at the Black Educators Awards for outstanding service and teaching.

And, as though what she had done was not bad enough, she had the nerve to add two additional charges against me. As I stated before, she thought that I had alcohol in my desk; but I am a typical teetotaler and never drank in my life. And as for the claim that I hit a child in my own class: I had never even raised my hands to my own kids, why would I hurt a child in my class?

After you handle all the appeal paperwork on your own to disprove the allegations against you, a hearing is scheduled where everyone involved is present. The hearing was in Brooklyn. The principal was supposed to be at the hearing, but she did not consider it worth her time and missed all three scheduled meetings where they were investigating my behavior. Each time a meeting was scheduled, I had to travel with my counselor, and each time she did not show, they claimed she had a good reason. Even the superintendent was unavailable. It really shows just how much respect they lack for teachers.

When the hearing finally happened, the opposing side — the principal and the superintendent — stated their case first. At that point, it felt as though I had committed terrible crimes and was on trial for my life.

Following their diatribes, my counselor spoke, answering each of the allegations in turn. I had just a few brief minutes to read my appeal and was not allowed to speak against any of the lies told about me. It was definitely a one-sided hearing — *their* side. I was guilty without a trial.

My counselor did nothing to help me and did not oppose them aggressively or even speak up for me. I felt betrayed and violated. What made it worse: I had to wait for the verdict to arrive in the mail.

Only after the sentence was passed, did I have the right to request the few minutes of the hearing on tape. Even so, the tape was unclear and hard to understand; appealing their verdict would be almost impossible.

After losing the appeal, I was terminated due to the U's but remained on payroll for the entire time, until the court reached their final decision. I could, however, still use my license; but who would hire someone with such a black mark against them? *No one!* Plus, I am sure that the principal had my name smeared all over the school system to make sure that no one would ever give me a chance.

Even when I was given several interviews in Westchester, I was not hired because the administrators contacted her, and she made sure they knew what had happened.   Now do you understand why I feel that life is just not worth living, and that it might be time to decide which combination of pills will end my suffering?

The next step was the Rubber Room. After being betrayed by my lawyer, who appeared to be on the wrong side of the table even though he sat next to me, I was then sent to teacher hell, or oblivion, for an unknown period until they passed a sentence on me and the others in this room. Which brings me to the present.

What Could Be Worse?

When you are sent into teaching oblivion, you are not alone; I realized that as I entered the Rubber Room. As I mentioned, another teacher from my school was also there. These rooms serve as holding cells, minus the bars, where we await our fates.

The unfair and scary part is that the people who are judging you have no real clue who you are or what you are capable of doing. Instead, they judge you based on the information provided to them by those who decided that you are no longer worth anything, that teaching is not for you; by those who want to discard you like yesterday's garbage, without the stink.

The really horrific part is that you cannot bring any witnesses, nor can you get anyone to testify on your behalf. At least real criminals can have their lawyers defend them in a real court of law, presenting a real case on the criminals' behalf. Supposedly, we were there because we presented a real physical and mental danger to the students: not in my case. There is no benefit of the doubt as to whether I or the others are innocent. The benefit of the doubt goes to the kids. However, there are no safeguards to protect the accused.

Virginia Green: Hear Her Voice

This is another account of what happened: decide for yourself the truth, as you learn the events that led up to Virginia being placed in this living prison.

Virginia is one of many teachers who have been wrongly accused of a crime. So many teachers get accused of doing so many things to students that, to supervisors, it has become necessary to punish the adults as they would a small child: *Send them to their room.* But, in this case, it is not the teachers' room — it is an isolated and barren place. You will soon read about the consequence of such a place to poor Virginia, who was accused of hitting one of her students and using alcohol as her beverage of the day.

Flashback

As Virginia took her seat in this horrific room, which had no windows, one long plastic table, metal chairs, and a bathroom for community use, her mind went back in time to where it all began.

The first day of school was always the most exciting one for both kids and teachers: the anticipation of a new school year, new students and teachers meeting each other, and setting the daily routines is often met with smiles and, sometimes, frowns.

Teachers begin by introducing themselves to their new students, setting up their daily routines and schedules, handing out textbooks, and placing a daily plan on the board. Next, rules of discipline — both rewards and consequences — are listed on a chart and the day officially begins. For Virginia Brown, this had become routine as it was her twentieth year in the school. And she was also excited because she was going to teach second grade for the first time.

The first few weeks passed without incident, and everything seemed to be working out. Virginia's class was very well behaved, her classroom was set up properly, and her lessons were informative and interesting. Her students were happy to have her as their teacher, and she readily answered their questions and helped those who struggled to understand anything that was taught.

But all of that came to an end after the holiday. Darren came from another school where he had been suspended for disruptive behavior. But no one told Virginia that.

Darren was cruel and divisive, and he manipulated his parents into believing that everyone was against him in his other school, and that they were just picking on him and making up stories that he did bad things. He had done more than his share of evil at that school, and with the help of his parents and their attorney, he got away with everything. Darren knew that he had everyone under his thumb. He used his craftiness and false smile to get what he wanted, no matter who got hurt.

Darren entered Virginia's class the first day back after holiday vacation. He was greeted by Virginia and given a seat next to a quiet little girl named Kati Rose. Kati was smart and could not stand anyone who did not want to learn or who was disruptive. Darren was a handsome, cute little boy who pretended to want to be her friend. So, Virginia asked Kati to help him get adjusted to the class, fix his notebooks the way she wanted them, and explain the daily routines and assignments expected to be completed each day.

But Darren had other ideas in mind. Every time Kati tried to explain something to him, he pretended to hear, but then lied and told the teacher that Kati was calling him names, that she was telling him the wrong things to do and trying to get him in trouble with his new teacher. Virginia did not quite believe him, but didn't want to call him a liar, so she spoke to Kati alone and asked her what happened.

Instead of believing Kati, Virginia called her mother and told her that Kati was becoming disruptive and picking on a new child in the class. You see, Kati was very smart, and some of the other kids hated her because they thought she was the teacher's pet, and they were happy to help Darren with his little scheme. It was really sad that what Virginia Green was doing to poor Kati Rose was what others would do to her in the future: assuming guilt by word of an untrustworthy student or adult out for revenge.

The Present

I opened my eyes and saw the bare walls, the angry faces, the despair and depression in the eyes of everyone placed, for whatever reasons, in this horrific place dubbed the Rubber Room. Why was I here? Let's start from the beginning, and you can decide whether my fate was just or if it had been sealed without any due process; if I was found guilty without a trial based solely on the word of someone so young and out for revenge.

If there is supposed to always be an investigation into allegations made by a student or parent against a teacher, why had I been sitting here for the last four weeks? No one wanted us around children because they claimed we were incompetent, dangerous, and insolent to supervisors who had personality conflicts with us and used us as examples to prove who was in charge and demonstrate their power. Sent to spend our days in a room that looked like a prison cell, we sat there staring at the walls, or reading books, or just crying, until the day was over. They were paying us our full salaries to sit in a room and mull over our guilt.

As I sat there contemplating my next step, I looked around the room and saw one woman knitting a sweater, a man on the phone with his real estate agent, and another drawing pictures. I sat down and began reading a novel I had always wanted to read, and then I walked around the room just to exercise and stretch. Many just sat staring at the walls, looking fragile and dejected.

One woman said she had been in the room for over one year and another said she had been there for about three weeks. Someone else said he could not remember how long he had been there, but it was at least four years.

At times, I wondered if it would have been better to just resign and get another job, but then they would have won. I believed that when you are innocent, you must fight. But there was no one to join in my fight; my attorney was definitely on the other side.

I began to feel like I was living someone else's life, watching it all happen from the sidelines. I began to contemplate what I would do for the rest of my life: definitely not sit and wait there for my world to collapse even more than it already had.

How could they expect educated people to sit in a room for days on end and just vegetate? Even vegetables grow and have a purpose in the scheme of things. But where were the antioxidants to help prevent me from getting sick and from developing serious conditions such as fear, depression, and anxiety?

From the feelings of fear, despair, and helplessness building inside me as I sat there each day reading just meaningless words and keeping a journal of my feelings and writing this memoir, I realized that my purpose now was to tell the world what happened to me and other teachers and to help prevent others from enduring the same pain.

Even though I couldn't teach any more, I thought I might as well do something fruitful with my time. I began authoring my story for all of you to read; judge me for yourself and decide whether I am really guilty or not.

For the previous three years, I had taught third graders. The students in my classes varied in range: some far above grade level, some middle level, and some far below third grade in both reading and math. However, for some reason, after reading the profile of the classes I was to teach, I realized that many of the students were far below grade level, and some were even non-readers. Of course, I never complained and knew that I would have my hands full and would need to create lessons to address the needs of all the students in my class.

Every evening, when I got home, I went online and researched different ways to work with children that were non-readers. I had taught first grade for many years and had the skills to work with these students. But I wanted material that they'd never used before and stories that would interest them. I found many websites that helped me address the needs of these students. I even approached the reading specialists in the school to see what help they could offer. The other third grade teachers did not have many students with these serious learning needs and gave me little support.

Because I really cared about my students, I decided to consult with the special education teachers to see if I could implement some of their reading materials in my class and perhaps borrow some of the beginning readers to work with my children. Not only were they helpful but they insisted that I observe them working with their students to get a better handle on how I could use their materials in my classroom.

I thought that I was doing the right thing, and, armed with more knowledge, materials, and help from others, I thought I would succeed. Working with my students, I realized that some of them needed more help than what I was giving them. One or two kids had problems focusing on the materials presented, three struggled with tracking, and two could not remember simple letters or sight words. And one was diagnosed with dyslexia. Naturally, I was up against a wall with no way out. Although I provided practice for the class, when the reading test was given, they struggled and could not really read the stories, much less answer questions about them.

One of the other teachers came into my room while my students were being tested with a warning I was supposed to heed — make sure your kids pass this test, no matter what you must do and no matter what it takes. Staring at her, I started to question what she had said but thought better of it. Repeating what she stated in a more emphatic tone, I realized what she was telling me and just thanked her for her message and her concern.

As the testing end time drew close, I wondered what harm it might do if I just gave them ten or fifteen more minutes. What would happen if I walked around, helping them get more answers correct? What would happen if I stood in the back of the room and read the stories out loud and made sure they knew which answers to pick? Who would I be hurting? And who would know what I did? The answer was staring me in the face as I went over to my closet and dried the dampness off my forehead and said to no one but myself: *I would!* Who would I be cheating? The precious students that I was teaching. Therefore, I would not compromise myself or my ethics by doing what the other teacher alluded to.

Collecting the test papers — on time — and placing them in the proper envelope, I thought about what that teacher had said. I heard her voice next door during the test; she was speaking very loudly. I began wondering, why would she be talking during a reading test? Unless … You figure out the rest.

The following week, the same thing next door happened during the math test. I heard many voices at the same time speaking to their students. I assumed that they might be reading the directions, questions, or instructions, or more. All you are supposed to do is explain how to take the test and explain any written instructions that are stated; you never read the math questions or the choices.

This time, one of the administrators came into my classroom and implied the same thing that the last person did during the reading test. She stated that she hoped my students would do well and that they were properly prepared, and that I should give them the best possible testing conditions and opportunities to pass. What was that supposed to mean? I assumed that was another one of her warnings to make sure they passed, since she had just given me a "U" rating on a math lesson that anyone else would have rated "S" or "O" for outstanding. She seemed to have it in for me and I had no idea why.

At the follow-up meeting, she claimed that the students looked confused during the lesson, and she could not follow the steps that I was teaching in simple addition with exchange. She claimed that I was all over the place and that the children were not paying attention, and that only a few of my students understood my practice problems. That was not true.

She even had the gall to tell me that they were unruly, which was not the case either. When I tried to defend myself and answer the points that she had stated on the written observation, she ignored me, saying we should move on and telling me to sign it. I did not.

I went to my union rep and asked for help. I'd never received a "U" rating in my life for anything. When I asked her how she would have presented the lesson, she stated that it was not her place to tell me how to do my job. But it was! One of her jobs *was* to help a failing teacher before casting them aside. I don't think she ever taught a day in her life, and if she did, I believe she was as totally ineffective then as she is now as the poorest excuse for a supervisor that ever existed.

After receiving my first "U" rating, I became very distraught and could not figure out what went wrong with my lesson. The supervisor stated in her observation letter that the aim of my lesson was unclear, that the focus areas did not match the aim, and that my motivation methods did not actually motivate anyone. She also stated that I did not use enough hands-on materials and manipulatives to teach the lesson.

Added to that, she claimed that a student was tapping his foot on the floor, and that by the end of the lesson, they were all doing the same thing, and because I had done nothing to stop it, it distracted the children easily. The kids were well behaved, and none of that happened.

I even had the math teacher review my lesson to ensure everything was in order. I did not have to, but I had heard horror stories about the supervisor's post-observation letters and discussions, and I wanted to cover all bases. Obviously, I left several out. Observed the principal did not comprehend how to create and follow a lesson plan or understand she did not even follow the lesson plan or the pre-observation discussions that preceded the lesson, nor did she pay close attention to the lesson being presented. Her eyes kept wandering to the clock on the back wall, and she looked totally bored.

Most supervisors wrote notes during the lesson and created a post-observation letter with positive points and, of course, negative points. Those that want to be more constructive in their comments will create suggestions for the teacher in order to improve their lessons in the future. My letter was filled with everything that I did wrong and nothing that I did right — except show up for work.

I enlisted the aid of my chapter leader and asked if she would help me write a rebuttal letter answering each of her negative points one at a time. But the chapter chairman was of no help either. It appeared that everyone was against me, as though there was some conspiracy to eliminate me from the profession, to obliterate me from this world. I had no idea what I could have done to deserve this horrible treatment, and I had no idea how to find out. My lawyer was useless and could not care less. He was not going to profit from this case, so why would he even try to assist and exonerate me from a crime that I did not commit?

All of sudden, as I sat there in the Rubber Room, I saw a shadow in the corner of the room. The face appeared out of nowhere. The smile on that face was evil and quite telling: the person knew something about me, I could feel it. A chill went up and down my spine as I sat on the hard metal chair, my back hurting, wondering when this torment would end. I was beginning to think that I just might end it all myself.

Depression can set in when you are stressed, have financial worries, lose a loved one, or, in my case, are wrongly accused of a crime. Having no recourse and no one who cared about what happened to me assist me, I started to believe that my life was worthless, that I really had no purpose being here anymore, and that I did not want to return here even one more day. The people in this room were using the time to create new businesses for themselves, write their memoirs to be published, or buy stocks on their cell phones. How creative of them to do this right under the eyes of these guards who were evil, the other victims of this abuse, and the sinister face at the door.

When the day ended, I became leery about walking to the bus stop alone. A chill went up my spine, and I began to feel cold. I had no idea why I had this feeling, but something told me I was in danger and that I had better be alert and make sure that I was not being followed. I could feel someone's eyes penetrating my back as I walked to my bus stop and got on the bus.

Sitting in the back would allow me to see anyone coming on or going off the bus. Right before the doors were about to close, a young man wearing a hooded jacket and a dark sweatshirt banged on the door and was allowed onto the bus. His eyes were bloodshot, and he gave me an eerie feeling. He stared right at me, and I knew that I was in deep trouble and had to react fast. I changed to a seat next to an elderly woman and tried to start up a conversation with her, but she just wanted to sit quietly and relax. So, I got up and sat closer to the bus driver, but he ignored me too.

Trying to catch his attention, I did not notice the young man moving closer to where I was sitting. By sitting right behind the driver, I thought I was safe: the seats were positioned sideways, and I was right in front of the door so that I could leave the bus at the next stop. But what would I do after that and what would happen if he followed me?

I called my husband on my cell phone and explained my fears to him. He said he was too busy to listen to my paranoia and hung up on me. I called my two daughters, and my mom after that, and the same thing happened. It was as if I became the pariah in the family since I had been in that dreaded Rubber Room. The solution became clear. Only one thing left to do, and I figured today was as good a day as any to do it.

***

Feeling despondent and dejected when I finally arrived home has brought me to where I am right now: sitting on my bed with all these colors in front of me so I can decide which ones to take first.

It does not really matter where I start. As I take a red and blue pill, I hear a loud bang and then another noise coming from the other room; someone is in my house. I must have left the door open. That strange boy must have followed me home.

No, I am positive I did not leave the door open — I locked it so no one would disturb me. Looking up, I stare into the cold and calculating eyes of that same young man from the bus. He has several bottles in his hands and starts to pour out the many pretty colors. He hands me some water and about ten different pills. I do not care what they are or what they do. I just swallow them.

You can guess the rest.

Leaving me on the bed, he turns and gives me a demonic grin. He makes one phone call and leaves. It's finally done! Murder or suicide? The end result is the same.

Epilogue

Many teachers are accused of doing the wrong thing by administrators and are removed from the classroom for different reasons. Virginia would not do something that the other teachers on her grade did, and this cost her more than just her job. Recourse, as you can tell, is hard, and the person is considered guilty until proven innocent. More than unfair, it is quite unjust.

To all educators who have ever been wrongly accused and to the memory of a good friend who this happened to: I dedicate this story and hope no one goes through what Virginia did, and that principals give their staff members a chance to explain before bringing down the ax.

The third face is behind the large pink granite stone, the one with dancing shoes, book covers, and some flowers on top. There are some apology notes and cards attached to each side. Some are from her tormenters and others are from family — too little too late.

This is Belinda's story, hear her voice before this happens to someone you love.

Tortured and Betrayed

Belinda's Story

My life as a teen is so difficult. What did I do to deserve so many tortures? First, being sixteen is not easy: temptations fly in front of my face, and everyone tells me it is up to me to decide whether to succumb to what they refer to as peer pressure, going along with the crowd, or, heaven help us, thinking for myself. Drugs, alcohol, and sex are front and foremost on the minds of many teens. What some of my friends are into, I am not.

Many use recreational drugs, smoke pot, and even have an occasional drink. I really don't see the appeal of ruining my lungs and risking getting a fatal disease, drinking to get liver problems, or having sex and getting a communicable disease, or worse still — pregnant. But that's just me; and then there is everyone else.

I love parties just like the next person, but lately I have been passing on many of them since I am not into a lot of what happens there. I guess that makes me weird or a freak or maybe I'm just someone with an independent mind. How strange is that?

Learning to deal with these added pressures makes being a teenager difficult. I think they need to write a manual of instructions to help us figure out what we are supposed to be doing opposed to what we are not. Deciding whether to go along with the crowd is an issue I now face. But, even worse is having no one to share my thoughts, fears, and questions with. You see, the one person that I had is gone. That was my sister, Marcia, but I will tell you about her later.

My mom is great, but you know how old people can be. She will discuss certain topics with me but not others. For example: PMS. Well, that is one area I am an expert on and do not need any help to define. Dealing with this wonderful prize makes me wonder what women and girls ever did wrong to deserve this pain, torture, and hormone screw-up with bloating and munchies every month. Craving sweets such as candy and chocolate and foods filled with tons of sugar and salt appease me; but gaining weight and my stomach looking like a water balloon is not a great perk.

Next, of course, are the wonderful bodily changes that occur. In my case, at age ten I looked like I was at least 16. Think about going to school with size 34 DDs jutting out in front of you, and all the stares you get from the boys in your class. Yeah, 34 DDs! Imagine that on a girl who is only five feet tall and weighs too much as it is. Growing up just happened too fast for me.

This morning I woke up feeling down. My normally perky mood has disappeared. Why? Let's get into why. I, Bertha, am still having trouble socializing, and now my latest problem is I have no date for the junior prom.

Dating: the dreaded "no date for the weekend, the prom, or a party." How traumatic is that? Is it okay to go alone?

Well, the prom is just three days away, and I do not have a glimmer of hope for getting a date. I have been told that to go stag (alone) is not wise. I really do not care, but since I do not want to put myself in a position where others make fun of me or criticize me for not having a date, I think I will just pass on the entire occasion.

I know many teens like me feel the same way. And yet others have the courage to take a stand against those mean, popular girls who cannot see past their makeup, hairstyles, figures, and clothes.

Dating is serious and knowing the right way to act and control yourself is important. I wish my sister were here, but now she's gone away to college, so I'm all alone. She had tons of dates in high school, but I have never even been asked to go on a walk or go to the movies.

My mom told both of us to go out only in groups and to never be alone on a first date or even the second. We are both too young to really understand the seriousness of what could happen if you are alone in a car with a boy, or even at a party where things could, and sometimes do, get out of control. She instructed my sister, who listened, to always have her phone charged, never drink or smoke, and not be influenced into doing something just to keep a boy in her life or to fit in with the group.

So, what do I do? I still have no idea, and as I said, the prom is in three days. I have asked some other kids to weigh in, and here is what they have to say on the issue:

> Susan: I would never go to a prom by myself. I would be too embarrassed.
>
> Joanie: I would go to the prom with a group of girls, and we could still have fun dancing and enjoy the food and just being with friends.
>
> Maggie: You'd never catch me without a date.
>
> Joyce: I would take my brother or a cousin that no one knows before I'd go alone.
>
> Faith: I would never go alone to a prom. I would rather stay home.

Many girls feel they would be made fun of if they went to the prom or a dance without a date. They never think there could be some guys who just want to hang out and not be bothered with a date, flowers and all that. They might go just to hang out with their friends. And who knows, they might just have some real fun with someone nice.

The only way I could go to the prom would be ... well, that's not an option anymore. I decided to put on my prom dress, fix my hair and makeup, play my favorite song, and then lie down on my bed and wait.

Now I feel no more pain.

Epilogue

Many girls and even guys are conscious of how they look and want to be accepted by the cool, popular crowd. Belinda had a pretty face but a poor self-image, and when others commented on her appearance, clothes and such, she would cower. There was no one there to defend her or explain to her that she was fine just the way she was. Pressure to have a date for the prom is not uncommon, and many girls feel ostracized and dejected when they attend these events alone or with a group of friends.

Unfortunately, Belinda took the wrong way out. To all those girls who are mean, cruel, and help create the problems that caused Belinda to take her own life: read this and think before you do it to someone else. It could happen to you!

Framed: The Principal

I spent the last ten years as the principal of a school in the Bronx, only to be forced out for not being corrupt, as you will soon learn.

Every year, the fifth grade takes a statewide writing test, and the tests are carefully monitored and scored. The testing coordinator goes from room to room, making sure the students and teachers know how to administer the test and how to package it. The test coordinator prepares the tests in separate envelopes to be scored by a group of staff members who are not on the fifth-grade staff.

The testing coordinator explains the scoring process, the rubrics, and how each grade is to be determined when scoring each paper. After that, each member of the scoring team receives a certain number of tests to score.

A special time and place is set aside for the scoring and only the members of the team are allowed in the room. I, as the principal, was asked to help score the tests. At the end, the testing coordinator collected all of the tests and scrap paper, and then generated each child's score using the class list. The scores were placed on the scoring sheets, along with their names.

Generating the lists and placing the scores on the class list was step one. I insisted that the test coordinator place the student's scores on the scoring sheets that go to the board in my office; after that, the assistant principal took the package to the district board to be scored.

The only process left was to handle getting the students who were absent to take makeup tests. That was the job of the testing coordinator.

She gave me a set of the scores on the class lists and kept another in her file. This should have been the end of it. However, about three weeks later, the testing coordinator received a phone call. The voice on the other line said, "I'm Jennifer, the head of testing at the Board of Ed, and Mr. K here represents the office of the Chancellor."

"What is the nature of this call? Why are you reaching out to me?" the coordinator asked.

"We are concerned about the scores. We feel that three classes of students did not meet the right criteria and we think you should reassess the tests and have another team rescore them."

"Why?"

"We are not happy that so many failed, and we think they might have been scored incorrectly or possibly the team of teachers did not understand the scoring procedure."

"That is not true. I went over the rubric, gave them examples for each grade, and monitored the scoring myself. Any indecision I handled and had someone else check and score. What are you suggesting I do?"

"We would like you to rescore them."

"I'm going to conference my principal in on this call, and see what she says about what you are suggesting." After the principal got on the line, the call continued.

"We feel that either you should amend the tests. We will send you a list of the students' names who had low scores, and then you can add one point to the scores that are ones, twos, and threes."

"In other words, you want me to change the scores to make it look as if the students passed the test even though they did not? I want to make sure I've got this right: you want me to make a duplicate set of scoring sheets but add one point to each score of one, two or three?"

"That's exactly what we want you to do. Dr. E, what is your thought?"

"*Never!* The children's scores must stay as they are. They need the help next year. You are making the wrong choice, but if that is your final word, we will take it up with the chancellor and the state."

They hung up.

I went to Dr. E's office and thanked her for backing me up, but little did we know this was not the end of it.

Two weeks later with Dr. E.

The state department sent me a letter telling me to require the head of testing to gather all of the fifth grade and special ed practice tests, test booklets, and any scrap paper associated with the test, and send everything in one package to the state so that how these tests were scored could be investigated.

I was livid, but what could I do? It took two days to get what they asked done, and then I sent it off to the state. As the principal of this school, I am the one responsible for the entire testing program, and making sure that it is done fairly and honestly. The team of teachers who graded the tests were not from grade five, and the test coordinator and I oversaw the scoring. Only those scoring were allowed in the room, and the tests were evenly distributed. The teachers did not know all of the students whose tests they scored.

About a month later, right before the summer vacation, I received a letter from the state department staying that every score was accurate, and they would not change even one. They also apologized for questioning the scores. I thought this was the end of my woes, but it was not.

I began receiving odd phone calls at work with strange, threatening messages. The voice said that I'd better retire or I would find myself a suspect in a financial crime involving the books, budget, and more. At first, I thought it was someone trying to shake me up because of what happened with the test scores.

I began going over my financial documents and found that nothing had changed. The voice claimed that they had copies of my budget and paperwork showing where the money went. They said that some of the figures did not add up.

Someone must have made copies and changed my accounting, which I reviewed with a certified public account, who did not know it was changed before handing it to the district person in charge. I began to think that this person who changed my figures was trying to get me out of my job. But why?

The calls continued, and I even got some at home. The person that called did not have a blocked number, so it must have been a burner phone of some type. I alerted the police.

At this point, I did not want to throw in the towel, but my family felt it was the right way to go. I called the district asking that my reading and test coordinator promoted to intern assistant principle. It never happened. She, too, was a victim of the testing supervisor's actions at the board.

For the remaining years I was there, the reading scores continued going up, and when I left the school they were 60 percent, which was at or above grade level. If you looked at them even just a year or two later, you would see that the school dropped to the lowest quartile.

Burn: Let the Flames Reign

Arson — the crime of maliciously, voluntarily, and willfully setting fire to a building or other property for an improper reason or for a purpose, such as collecting insurance money.

Burn — To undergo rapid combustion or consume fuel in such as wry to give off heat, gases, and usually light; to be on fire.

I stood looking at that magnificent fire, watching the flames soar and take over the entire building as the structure was enveloped in a sea of orange, red, brown, and then ash. Smelling the smoke, I saw the soot and carnage that was created, and my job was done — now I watch as it all unfolds.

Problem solved. I left the scene, but not before I heard sirens blaring in the night air and the survivors of the fire alight from the building. I saw fear, despair, and hopelessness in their faces. I smiled. Finally, the revenge for all they put me through.

You can call me Jack. My hobby is arson and the sight of burning buildings and businesses brings a smile to my face. I love to create flames and fires in homes, but not before making sure the people have their fire insurance paid up. You see, up until I was caught, *I had a good thing going.*

The people living in those rundown and dilapidated neighborhoods were looking for ways to get out, make some money, and beat the insurance companies. Everyone knew that I was a fireman, it was true, but due to cutbacks, some of the men in my house were laid off, given desk jobs for less money, or just encouraged to retire. In my case, I retired and took the package they offered.

I have expensive tastes and so did my wife. She loved her sports cars. She made a decent salary working as a legal secretary to the president of a law firm, but she was selfish and greedy and wanted more. So, I decided to get her more — more space, a lot of it, if you know what I mean.

My client was Mr. P, who was down on his luck and needed some help. But I was not sure I could trust him. He called me on the cell phone I used for those special jobs, and I arranged to meet him at ten at the local pub.

After he left his office, he met me there, where we sat in the corner, hoping no one would hear our conversation. He laid out what he needed me to do and what the outcome would be. He had a garage where he kept wood for a fireplace and old leaves in a bag. He had lighter fluid, matches, and other flammables on hand in case he wanted to burn his leaves, use his trip, or light his fireplace. But I knew Mr. P was going to be careless; or at least he hoped that I would become *careless* and make sure that his house burned to the ground if no one got in. With a simple handshake, we agreed on the date, time, and price for my services.

Now, I bet you think that I had it figured out. Think again.

I went through all the supplies that I needed to complete the job and make sure that everything burned to the ground with no one would getting hurt or being the wiser. The next morning, I prepared my supplies and looked over the plan of executing the fire, making sure that everything was in place. I contacted the client and double checked the time, asking for a down payment, and then I went about preparing my supplies. Getting dressed, I ate a quick snake, had some coffee, and went to the house in question.

I did not see or hear anything inside the house — I was told to create the diversion and fire in the garage, where all the wood and flammables were kept. Using the lighter fluid, matches, and dried leaves that the owner had left in the garage (instead of outside for pickup), I went about setting the fire.

No one was around; the neighbors were out of town for a week, and one neighbor was in the hospital.

Though it was a residential area, there were very few houses on each block, and trees and fences surrounded the area, so it would be almost impossible to see another house, let alone inside the windows where I was working. The best part was that it was cold and cloudy; there were dark cumulous clouds above. Being a dead-end street, only the cars that belonged to Mr. P, whose house I was in, would come down the street. And there was only one car parked in the street; no one was there, as far as I could see, and it was in front of the vacant house that I believe belonged to the women in the hospital. Before I set the final match and lit the embers, I checked everything, then walked to my car and just waited.

The end came quickly as the house became enveloped in flames, and the buses around the perimeter were filled with dead leaves. The result was a huge, towering inferno.

I made sure that the house was gone and that no evidence linked back to me; I thought I was home free. As I returned home and took a shower to get all the ash and smoke off of me, I phoned the client and demanded payment. What happened, though, was something I never expected.

I made a mistake opening the door. Payment was made by Mr. P., but not in the way you think. After all, I was doing a service — getting the job done and the house burned — and the insurance money would be paid. But some debts are paid in full, and mine was paid as a Face Behind the Stone. My driver, Mr. Z, just smiled as he drove away with Mr. P in the back seat.

You see, had I looked up even for a minute when starting the fire, I might have seen the young girl at the window peering down at me. She never knew what happened: as the flames spread, the window blew out, and the result … you can only imagine. The basement was supposed to be empty but what can I say? Mr. P had not planned for his son's return from college, or his daughter's return, a day early, from a business trip. There bodies burned beyond recognition; at least their ends came quick.

Epilogue

Arson is wrong and using it to collect insurance is more than wrong. In this case, many died because of my fee and the greed of one man. Others would follow, as someone else would take my place and earn the fee, but hopefully they would be more careful before they set the fire. Arsonists are deadly and dangerous and often do not get caught.

PART 2

The Voices Behind the Stones Need to be Heard

The World of Gloom and Despair

Prologue

How did Bea get to this place and why is she walking around this cemetery? Why are the graves unmarked?

Walking outside and looking at her surroundings, the stench, the grime, she sees the arrival of darkness that has engulfed the overcast sky, the dark clouds, the night. She is walking through an old cemetery, and the silence is deafening as it embraces the cemetery along with frigid air. Each grave has a marker, but the names and dates are hidden by mold, mildew, and thick fog. Those buried are past participants in the show and warranted their result.

The cracks in the pavement as she walks past each grave create an eerie sound. The sky is pitch black, and the inscriptions on each stone begin to radiate a glow. Tall trees, gnarled branches, and decaying leaves have all turned into a muddy-looking substance, a mildew and rotten odor that has permeated throughout the cemetery.

But something is drawing her to one grave. A grave that has just been dug, the coffin lying above the ground and the lid opened. The stone engraved with a name. Chills come all over her. She can't stop shaking. Who is going see what's behind her mask?

The path of weeds behind her dilapidated cabin is surrounded by trees with dead branches. The howling winds, the faint scratching sounds on my windowpanes as the door creaks and blows open in the wintry darkness. The furniture is worn, the bedroom needs painting, and the headboard is cracked, making it hard to put her head back and forcing her to sleep on the opposite side.

Outside her doorway is a clearing in the wooded area with an undergrowth of grass that looks brown and decayed that leads to a cemetery. She ended up here, but why? How did she manage to find this small cemetery? Where did she live before the cabin?

A face forms in Bea's mind as she thinks about the past. It haunts her dreams as she sees *him*, with his hollow looking eyes, his burnt skin, and his gnarled hands. He's out there, somewhere, creating fear, terror, and violence. She can hear the screams, the terror of those he tortured.

Yesterday, she closed her door and bolted it shut and blocked out the night noises as she prepared for bed and what she must do the next day — visit the graves. Those graves haunt her every waking hour. Just who are buried there? Bea alone will determine who gets that last grave. All that are buried in this cemetery are there because they did horrible things in life and were placed there without markers. They are the infidels.

Now the gravestones stand silently in the darkness, as icy wind blows the dead leaves covering some of the stones. She stands out here in the cold, listening to the howling wind, but her mind drifts back to where it all began and how she came to be here. As the darkness surrounds her, the clouds darken and the rain pours down, all over her — yet she feels nothing. Her mind is beginning to drift, she is fading away to a past that she hoped to forget, remembering the deeds that plague her in the present.

The air has a rancid smell, and the dust from it feels dry and thick as it touches Bea's lips. She is standing in front of an old stone front, when she feels a cold hand on her shoulder, and she begins to shake and shutter. The hand has a gentle yet firm touch, and the voice and words make her shiver. "You and you alone are responsible for these deaths and why they are paying and have paid for their crimes," the voice says. The puff of breath on her neck, and the sensation that burns through her body, causing a cold chill to go throughout her. Her eyes freeze, and her lips turn to ice.

Walking back to the entrance of the cemetery, Bea shivers in the cold, trying to process what to do next and how she will fulfill what she has been told. Each grave is unmarked, and each person in each grave deserved their fate.

Imagine living in a world like hers, filled with darkness and gloom. As the storm begins to rage, she realizes that this world is the only one left. The population is practically nil, and these nine people deserved their fate because of their crimes and abuse in the world that had once been filled with sunshine, light, beaches, parks, and trees with multi-colored leaves in the fall, snowcapped leaves in the winter, and green leaves in the summer. Now the trees are filled with falling dead leaves, bare and rotten branches, and overgrown weeds spreading in grassy spots.

No one smiles; that is, the few that survived the horrors that came before. And now they wander the streets until someone can find a place for them in a dark and depressing building with little heat, some food provisions, and beds for them, and until someone decide what's next. What did these people do? Why is one grave not filled?

This is the world most are living in as some of the population returns but to this grave environment. A world of gloom, darkness, dead leaves, and brown grass, and a forest of dead trees with brown leaves and a stench that will make one cower. Some people even have no sun — just darkness and no warm air. Some have scorching desert heat. As a result of the pandemic, there are so many changes to adjust to, including not being able to just enjoy the sunshine at times without having to cover one's face.

If you were the only person alive and had to live in the world like this, would you? You would experience blackness on the shoreline and the sand eroded on the beach looking darker than a brown crayon. No sun, just dark clouds and no visible light. The sun is gone, and the world is hidden in a veil of darkness.

The next time you walk outside, smell the fresh air, feel the sun in the sky hitting your face and giving you warmth, watch the animals walking by and the people on their way to work; and then think about never having these experiences again. Welcome to the future in this dark world, as you meet the man who will guide you to your new homes, explain the current rules that exist, and tell you what happens if you do not adhere to them or try and leave.

The sun does not warm this place because the trees are so tall and the branches and leaves so plentiful, overlapping each other, that it is hard to see past the top of the trees, which are over ten feet tall. The air is moist and smells foul, making it difficult to be outdoors at times. The cemetery is off limits and certain areas are too. The only people here are the felons.

The felons are grouped according to age, size of family, and educational ability, as well as skills. They are here because of what they did, and you will understand their crimes and dark secrets, and lies will be revealed.

Bea's face is covered; no one will ever see beneath her mask. But this place is not what it appears to be. It is run like a prison camp. You see, these people are guilty of crimes. Some more serious than others. Most of the felons are not sure why they have been sent here.

Bea wants to learn more about these people and the gravity of their crimes, and to unveil any secrets they are hiding. Her mask is like a safety net to protect predators from finding out who they really are, her own deep dark secrets, and much more.

A sudden noise has brought her thoughts back to the present, back to her surroundings. Someone was screaming and no one seemed to move in the direction of that scream to find out who was in trouble or being attacked. Everyone seems to be drifting in their own private world, some oblivious to even their own family members, others just walking aimlessly in the darkness of this world. One of these faces will be placed behind the last stone.

The Residents

There are currently five felons in this community — or town — who will have a place to live. They are given specific outerwear and tags with their names, ages and pictures. Their families are unfortunately here too.

They are all felons and have been sentenced to this place instead of a jail to serve their time. Their time is endless, and they will never be released from here ... ever. There is Oscar, a former presser and spotter in a cleaning store; Terrence, a known serial killer; Marcus, a bartender; Frederick, the undertaker; and, finally, Brad, the mechanic.

Four of the five had regular professions, or at least they appeared to be legitimate professions. But each one harbored hate and resentment against their customers, relatives, and people in general; this helped rationalize their thinking and justify their actions, at least to themselves.

Oscar had a way of getting even with customers who complained that their clothes were not pressed the right way. He would hang them up but incorrectly. Complaints were noted. And then he added a special ingredient to the spotting spray that contained no smell but would make the wearer sick — or worse. No one ever knew he did it nor did anyone realize why people got sick. So how did they find out? After getting drunk with his girlfriend one night, he did not realize she was the daughter of one of his customers who died recently. He told her all, not thinking she would ever turn on him. Loose lips sink ships.

The next is Terrence, a serial killer who went after older men and women for no apparent reason other than to eliminate them from this world, stating they had no purpose in life anymore and were draining the healthcare system for their own benefit and more.

Next, we meet our bartender, who was the most ingenious of all five. Marcus had a pal that worked for the mob — or the man who owned the streets, businesses, and more — and who had started another illegal venture. To pay off his own debt to this man, and to get the street business he needed to keep his bar running, Marcus had to do this man favors or lose it all.

And then there is Zack, who used his escort service for clients to not only enjoy the girls but also get drugs to sell on the street to young school kids. Frederick, the undertaker, was an original. He would get the bodies ready for viewing — dressed, makeup and all — making sure that no one saw what he did under the clothing. He stole the hearts, livers, bladders, and other internal organs to be sold on the black market for those in need of organs. Waiting on the donor lists was not an option for some, who would pay thousands or more for this solution.

Finally, we come to the worst one of all: Brad, the mechanic, who would fix your car but, if you questioned the price, dared to challenge his abilities, or said he "better not mess up your car and just fix it," well … you know brakes can fail after a while, gas tanks can leak, and steering wheels might get stuck.

There you have them.

Each felon arrived accompanied by a prison guard, handcuffed, his personal items in the hands of the guard. All five had the look of a dangerous killer, and yet they were calm. They had no idea what was in store for them, or why they were sent to this island and not a prison.   Bea wonders what her role is. *Am I to deal with these men? Is there a reason why I have been chosen? Did I commit a crime, and this is my penance?*

The men are being housed in a small area in separate cells. They cannot face each other, no conversations are allowed, and the rules will be spelled out. Is she the one making them? She feels like she is in a bad movie and waiting for something to happen.

Bea is next. She wonders, *Why am I handcuffed and placed in a cell? What in the world did I do?* They have not said a word to her.

She overhears two of the guards talking. "He paid a lot to get rid of her," one says. "She was in the way of his social life and extra-curricular fun. With her out of the way, he can spend all her pension, her savings, and then if something happens to her, the ten million in life insurance her parents left her."

How am I ever going to get free? she wonders. *What will I do? And if I try to escape, will they shoot to kill, making the man I thought I knew quite rich? Who can I trust?*

What that her husband did not know was Bea has documents safely put away stating that if something happens to her, it is her husband's fault, and to investigate it as a murder.

Lying on the awful cot with the threadbare blanket, Bea begins to think. She knows that even though they gave her a pad and pen and books to read (odd, she thinks), she could not write down a plan without someone reading what she wrote. So she will pretend to be an author writing a novel and tell them that her publisher will publish it even though Bea is here. But they will not tell her what my crime was; she can only gather information from what she hears when they talk about her.

Slowly planning her thoughts, she walks over to the small closet — these cells were like small rooms in a hospital, where you can store stuff — and she notices someone before her must have left clothes, shoes, and other things. She might be able to use these to disguise herself, if only she could figure out how to escape without being seen.

No one has realized that this stuff was already there; everyone is allowed to bring a few personal items, so if they see these things, she will say they are hers. Luckily, the person was her size. She wonders, *how can I escape and where will I go?* Out of nowhere, someone else appears: an odd-looking man with a strange smile. He says, "I'm here with a message from your husband. He is here to take you out, to rid himself of a problem. Namely, you.

"I kill people for the fun of it. It does not matter why or for what reason. They could have given me a wrong look or asked for money for coffee or even just rubbed me the wrong way. One time, I was walking home from work, never mind where, around 1 a.m., and there was a man sitting on the sidewalk. He stuck his hand out and I shot him in the head and kept going. One less for the world to feed and deal with.

"The next morning, it poured, and I was getting into my car, when someone snuck up behind me just to say hello. I stabbed him because I thought he was going to try and rob me.

Not true, he was my neighbor, and it was time to rid the world of this pompous pest. Every day, I wondered what possessed me to kill, and then I realized I just did it for the fun of it, to see how long I would get away with something I felt was a sport — or maybe my job — to rid the world of people that just don't count.

All my life, I felt alone and not wanted, and my parents sent me off to boarding school, where I was kicked out for fighting and not following the rules. No friends, and no one to defend me when I was accused of starting the fight. At this point, I realized that I would take out my anger on anyone that dared to cross me or not give me what I wanted, or just because I felt like it. So, what if they are innocent victims. So, what if they are dead and mourned. Who cares? Why should I care?

"I even killed a dog a kid let off its leash in the kid's front yard. The poor kid ran inside the house and shouted and cried, but when his parents came out, the dog was gone. You can figure out how and why. Killing is an art, or a sport; it is creativity, and my method of killing has stumped the police for years. I might be behind this stone telling all this to you, but what I did will haunt the world and this town forever.

"So dear Bea, it's time to fulfill my contract with your husband, and then deal with the others present on this island, who are trying to add me as the last person in the last grave."

The smile on the man's face and the scar on the left side of his neck were both terrifying. Bea's heart was racing, and her pressure was rising.

There are nine buried below the ground, and there are no names or markers. Bea starts to feel odd, and someone gives her some water, but what was in it? Feeling weird and seeing double, Bea feels someone lift her up and throw her down a deep hole, into the same places where the nine were buried — or so you might think.

Opening her eyes as she falls hard on the ground, Bea finds herself in a dark and dingy place. Where is this? Looks like some sort of underground cemetery with coffins lined up and people lying in each one, but none are dead. Her name is embossed on the last one all the way to the left. The others just stare at her. How did she get here? What is the reason for the others being here, with coffins as their beds and small tables on each side, containing person items they feel they need.

One man speaks, and she hears a voice that sounds hollow, almost deathlike. Looking into his eyes, Bea sees no expression, just a face and lips moving. "You are here because you committed some type of crime, and to survive, you need to follow the rules set for all of us."

"Are you the spokesman for this group?" Bea asks.

"Let me just say you will hear them. Just listen carefully because you won't get a second chance if you break the rules, and you must memorize what you see and hear. Understand that you only get to hear them once. Ask no questions."

From somewhere distant, a voice could be heard, and this is what Bea is told: "Stay in your own corner, do not talk with the others for any reason, food will be provided (never mind how or where it comes from, it just does), keep your area clean, there is a small sink with cleaning supplies for yourself and your area. There is a community bathroom to relieve yourself, but before you enter, you need to ask the person that is in charge at the time. Keep your curtain closed and do not enter anyone else's area. Speak only when spoken to, which will not be often. We have a small library of books, magazines, and papers, but only the person in charge can access them. Do you understand? Say yes or no?"

"I got it, yes," Bea says. Moving to her corner all the way to the left and ignoring the others, Bea sits inside her coffin bed and cries her eyes out. Sent to this horrible place because her husband claimed she tried to kill him for the life insurance was his way of getting rid of her. With his connections and the one person who created this horrible place — Drake, the serial killer from above — her husband managed to get rid of a kind and wonderful person. He had said he needed to meet a friend in a hospital and Bea began to wonder why her husband found himself in the ER twice a week. He claimed that he was bringing the friend he worked with their things from his hardware store, like bulbs, extension cords, and more, and she asked to accompany him the next time he went there, claiming she had a pain in her arm.

The nurse who came flying out of the room when she saw Bea's husband then took a step back when she saw Bea; she approached Bea's husband, pretending she did not know him, and took Bea into a room. The nurse was not very friendly and rough on Bea's arm when checking it out, and Bea saw the look that she gave her husband and asked that someone else take care of her issues.

Things got out of hand when a security guard took Bea by the shoulders, tied her hands behind her back, and claimed she was yelling and screaming at the nurse, who was caring for her. It was all rehearsed: her husband signaling the guard to take hold of the situation, then calling the police, claiming that Bea picked up a needle and other sharp objects, aiming them at her husband and the nurse. It resulted in her arrest and led to where she is now.

So now she must figure out how food gets down there, how to escape, and what her next move is after that. Is there any way to find out how she got down there? Where is the hole, or whatever it is, that they dropped her down? On both sides, at the end of each row, there is a dark glass wall: is there a way to open it? Just how solid was it, and why didn't anyone try to escape?

Bea checks out the glass door down the way from where her coffin-bed was placed. She feels cold air coming from the bottom of it but can't reach the top or see if the door would slide open. There must be some type of cameras there because she has the feeling that her movements are being monitored. Suddenly, the man who brought her there is standing right in front of her and has forced the other captives to stand in a straight line.

He says, "Now you will understand why you are here because of what you did on earth before you were thrown down here. You will understand what the five felons occupying your cells will endure if one of you are brave and bold enough to join me in what I have planned for one."

While Bea and the others are listening and deciding how to deal with what they were just told, the families and the felons on this island have to come to terms with what they are about to endure. The families will be placed on a different part of the island, and each will be responsible for taking care of their own section, planting and doing odd jobs for food after the first week, taking care of their rooms, and making sure that their children stay with them and do not wander off. The felons will be allowed time outside to do other jobs far away from their families; but at one point, things might change, and not only for the families, the felons, and those down below.

Things are not cut and dry, though, and the felons, who are not allowed to talk with each other, have managed a way to communicate by tapping and rapping, along with other ways, to figure out their own solution for escaping. The guards spend most of their days talking with each other, not really paying attention to the felons, and they have not realized what the felons have planned.

However, before the felons can continue with their plan, they learn the reason they are down below.

They are told that it is not because they committed a crime — they were framed because someone close to them, such as a family member, relative, colleague, or even child, wanted them out of the way to collect life insurance policies and take over their companies, or for other reasons.

When they find this out, the nine of them and Bea are shocked. And now, they will be given an opportunity for release. They will be allowed to come out of the ground and cemetery, to be changed in appearance so no one will recognize them, to be given jobs and a home; but in the end, they will each have the chance to get even with those who put them below the ground.

The shock on their faces is horrifying but no one has given anything away — they must stay calm. Their emotions in check, they have to decide their own course of action and what their fate will be. What will they decide? Will they agree to the terms of their release? What would you do?

This is just the beginning. It's far from over.

Drake!

STORY FIVE

Suicide: The Only Solution

This is John's story. His is the fourth face behind the flat stone in the last row of this section. John is a handsome young man; he just could not handle life anymore. It is time to listen to another teenager before he's silenced.
Hear his voice before it's too late!

Have you ever felt like life is hopeless, and you just want to give up? Are the pressures of going to school, living up to your parent's expectations, and pleasing your friends getting to be too much for you? Depression, fatigue, lack of energy set in — and you feel like you really want to do nothing but bury your head under the covers; or better yet, go off to another, more peaceful world?

My name is John. This is my story. Listen to me. Hear my words before it's too late. But will you?

My parents hate me. All they want is for me to become a doctor. I hate science. My father is a tyrant and insists that I go to medical school, and he said if I don't, he won't pay for my college education. My mom is a trophy wife. She is smart, sneaky, gorgeous, and twenty years younger than my overweight and rich father.

They have a marriage of, let's say, convenience. She gets the money and takes care of him once a week, and he gives her anything she wants. He's a famous plastic surgeon who needs more help than any surgeon could provide. He is totally ugly and not just in his physical appearance. Everyone seems afraid of him for whatever reason.

My father told me that under no circumstances can I ever do anything other than enter the medical field. He controls my allowance, my cell phone, and everything in this house. Why should I even go on? He hasn't even noticed that my grade point average dropped from an A to a C, or that I smoke and drink on the weekends.

If I ended it all, he probably would just write my death off as a tax deduction on his next return. But I won't make it that simple for him. If I decide to end it, I will make sure that he gets the blame and pays for my death in some way.

The Beginning of the End

Every weekend, my parents go away on some gambling junket, as they call it, with their rich and snooty friends, leaving me with either the maid or some caregiver that works for them. I often wonder why they just didn't give me up for adoption or sell me into slavery. I feel like an appendage that needs to be removed because it is infected and has no more use.

So why not just take all these pills, which are just sitting right on my mom's dressing table? For some reason, she leaves them out in a neat row. She has Ativan, Haldol, Vicodin, and many more assorted tranquilizers and painkillers that she uses when feeling stressed. Though I cannot understand what this plastic bubble with no brain must be stressed about, except maybe where to go to lunch and what to order. My dad has some fun with some of the women at work, but mom is either oblivious to his dalliances or does not really care because she gets everything, she wants in the end anyway.

She has her own agenda and life, and occasionally, they go on these gambling junkets and hopefully win some more money to add to their already huge bank accounts. No one really knows what either of them do with all of this money or where it really comes from.

All I know is that they have no time for me. They never really pay attention to me when they are home. They throw money at me to keep me happy, or at least they think I am happy. Well: this should get their attention!

So, where does that leave me? Let's see take a guess! Good night!

Epilogue

Suicide is never the answer to solving one's problems. Unfortunately, John's parents were too busy to see the signs that he might be in trouble, that he may have depression, poor grades, and more. Parents need to be more vigilant and watch for the warning signs that something might happen.

Teen suicide is the third leading cause of death for 15- to 24-year-olds. Suicide is the sixth leading cause of death for 5- to 14-year-olds. There are many pressures that both juniors and seniors face. These pressures can be strong or tense. Living up to what parents expect can be an added stress to many teens. Teachers, friends, and even clergy set high goals for teens, and all too often, they cannot meet them, causing depression, silence, and worse.

Students feel that they must get high grades, attain academic success in school, be popular, and excel in sports as well. Some push themselves so hard that they forget to remember who they are and what they want. They are so worried about being what everyone else expects that they are blind and strive for the goals set by others, rather than realistic ones they should set for themselves. Added to these school pressures are peer pressure, family issues like divorce, lack of money, and social issues. All of this is like taking a flame and watching it grow into a huge fire that cannot be put out.

Sixty percent of high school students have considered suicide. It does not matter whether one goes to public or private school. No one is immune. Those sent away to boarding school feel alone or isolated. Many do not have the support of friends and family at home. Several might be able to handle the huge workload, but others cannot. Getting into the right college weighs heavily on their minds.

Schools can prevent this problem in many ways. First the students, teachers and parents must really understand the warning signs of teen suicide.

Warning Signs

- Changes in eating habits
- Changes in sleeping habits
- Drug or alcohol abuse
- Personality changes
- Violent reactions
- Running away
- Talking back; rebelling
- Always bored
- Failing grades
- Trouble concentrating
- No interest in things they used to love to do and were concerned about; loss of interest in fun things

- Complaints about headaches, stomach pains, tired
- No desire to do anything
- Poor grades

One of the major causes of suicide in children is depression. Let's not leave out the high percentage of LGBTQ+ youths that attempt suicide too.

Late Warning Signs

- Talking about suicide or a plan
- Violent actions, running away
- Impulsive behavior
- Refuses help; feels beyond help
- Verbally states, "I'm a bad person," feels awful inside
- Says out loud, "I feel helpless, worthless, or hopeless"
- Does not accept praise or reward
- Verbal hints, such as, "It's no use"
- Sudden mood swings; happy one minute depressed the next
- Gives away favorite things
- Makes a will
- States, "I am going to kill myself"

Every school needs a suicide prevention program and to follow tips such as these:

- Written policies and procedures need to be established for responding to students at risk.

- Written policies and procedures that explain in detail how to respond should be posted.

- In school response teams that are trained to handle and respond quickly.

- Work together with community agencies such as mental health and crisis centers. Work with clergy and police.

- Parents need to become involved in suicide prevention strategies; school training of staff; staff needs updated information that is current.

- Staff members must work together to help recognize at-risk students.

- Educating the staff about the warning signs.

- Staff members must understand the referral procedures for reporting a possible or potential suicide. Make sure the staff know to whom they should refer the student.

- In-service training for students, parents and teachers.

- Curriculum for students to learn how to understand the warning signs, myths, facts, and risk factors.

Schools need information that deals with these problems and social issues, and where to get help. They also need to have screening programs to identify students who are at risk. School psychologists and guidance counselors must be aware of these screening tools and trained to use them.

Peer-assistance programs for at-risk students are imperative. Peer support groups are vital. When your friend states that things are piling up, listen and show them you understand. Encourage your friend to talk to other people, talk to you, and offer to go along with them when they talk to an adult. Establish some type of trust. Join the person in activities they normally like. They need to have fun. Let them know that you are not going away, and they cannot put you off. Tell them to talk to a third person, such as a friend, adult, or school official.

Listen to them and pay attention to their words. Don't let them be secretive. Express concern. Do not agree to keep suicidal thoughts or threats a secret. Don't call their bluff; they just might do it. Let them know that having them as a friend and alive means the world to you.

Other Ways to Help

- Encourage your friend to talk to school counselors.
- Talk to parents.
- Train students to recognize when a friend might need help.

- Look into youth support groups to help support at-risk teens.

- Partake in youth discussion groups to help teens that feel isolated and alone.

- Refer to suicide hot lines with trained personnel in schools and in communities.

Dee's Story

Dee went to bed that night hoping to avoid her parents and sister the next morning. She had her plans in mind for the day: skip school and meet her two friends at the mall to hang out. Tossing and turning in bed, and beginning to feel nauseous, Dee decided to make herself some tea and then went back to bed.

After a restless night, she awoke and got ready for the day, still not feeling great. Walking outside, she had no idea that she was about to enter a world with no sun nor darkness nor ice. With fear in her eyes, she realized she had no idea how she got to where she was. Thinking it was still a dream, she wandered aimlessly, but the more she walked, the colder she felt, and the darkness enveloped her within and on the outside.

Welcome, Dee, to your new world, where no one will care for you. No one to bring you food. A world filled with no hope, just people wandering around looking for something but with no idea what it is. You did not appreciate your family and school, and you chose the wrong paths; and in this world, you are all alone and will have to choose your own path to explore.

Dee found herself in the blackness of a shoreline, the sand eroded, the beach looking darker than a brown crayon. The sun was gone, and the world was hidden in a veil of darkness.

Though she was walking outside, the smell of the air was putrid. With coldness around her and no sun in the sky to hit her face and give her some warmth, she looked around and saw a different world. Faces covered with masks and people walking six feet apart, and yet others just pretending that nothing was happening.

Imagine waking up in your house and in it everything was gone. You found yourself sleeping on a hard, cold floor, and you had no idea how it happened. Your hands were frozen like solid ice, and all that was left on you were the clothes you slept in and four walls. No car, your garage empty, your family missing. And what happens next? You will be taken into worlds and places that will haunt you forever. Before the population became zero, find out what one man had experienced.

Each world this person entered was different. One with no sun, one with desert expanses, others with mist, dank air, and no power or electricity. Many lessons such as these could have been learned as Dee walked through her world, forever; she realized that she was never going back.

As she walked into the veil of clouds and darkness, Dee's eyes adjusted to her surroundings, and she had to decide where to live, to find out if there were any other people there, and how she would get food.

The world was hostile, and the people had their faces covered, and all she saw were their eyes. That was enough, though, to understand: no one came over to her, and some threatened her just with their looks. And then the unthinkable happened. She saw two familiar faces — so she thought — and hoped they would help her. But they just passed her by. With no place to live, she saw in this wilderness an empty shed, or maybe a barn, and she went inside and was taken by surprise: the faces of people from her past, sitting in rows, as if they were waiting for someone to speak. There was a podium and next to it… Oh, no, Dee thought. What is that?

Dee took a seat in the last row, but no one noticed her. She sat all alone. It was cold in there, and she felt a chill as a man in black robes stepped up to the podium and raised his arms above his head. He started to chant fiery words.

"This young lady was evil and deserves this painful ending," the man said. "Always hurting her pets, stamping on their limbs, fighting with her sister, and even breaking her sister's arms. In school, she was rude to all of you and made up lies that got you, Mr. Lee, almost fired. And you, Miss Smith, she claimed was having an affair with the assistant principal. Her lies got you transferred, but she got away scot-free.

"That is not all. All ten of you are welcome to say one sentence right to her face before I close this box and drop it six feet down in a hole with no marker. Her family is here, and they have prepared a celebration at their home following this service."

Dee wondered, *Who are they talking about? It can't be me? I never had Mr. Lee as a teacher or Miss Smith. Who are those people that look like my parents? Do they really hate me so much?*

I know I cut school and my choice of friends has not been the best. It has to be one of the girls who made up these lies. I need a closer look at their faces as they speak. Dee began to falter when she saw one of the faces staring up at her. *How could this happen? When did I die?*

The speeches were short, and each one said something awful about her. One said that she was rude in class, another said she cheated on tests, and the last one, a teacher, said that Dee threatened to call his wife because he was having an affair with a student. All lies. Dee screamed and yelled but no one heard her. Finally, her mother and father spoke.

"This is the happiest day of our lives," they said. "We are finally rid of this toxic waste."

Dee shriveled up inside: she could not believe what her parents said. From the back of the room, a woman entered and came up front. Dee met a boy, Nick, who was dating this girl named Marcy — and Nick decided to drop Marcy to become Dee's boyfriend.

The smile on Marcy's face said it all.

Dee walked up behind Marcy, who was sitting down with Nick at her side. *How is she going to get even? Is that possible?*

Dee began to chant to herself, and then … you won't believe what she did: holding a needle in her hand and dipping it in a liquid she had in her pocket, she approached Marcy. The smile on Dee's face was worse than that of Mary I of England or even Elizabeth Bathory — the most prolific killer of all time.

Walking behind Marcy, since no one could see her, Dee took the needle and stuck it in Marcy's neck, right in her throat. The life went out of her, no screams, no yelling; she just keeled over. The needle disappeared and left no mark.

A doctor, who was assigned to the funeral to look over Dee's sick parents and anyone else who might be harmed, declared Marcy's death from a heart attack; but only after the medical exam would it be confirmed.

Check out the face in the coffin before they close the lid.

Someone has an evil grin on her face.

The end … at least for now!

Don Smith

The Final Face Behind the Stone

Driving along, I saw one stone all by itself. No one seemed to have visited this stone. There are no flowers by the headstone, the grass is overgrown, and there are cobwebs and weeds all over the place. But, if you listen, you will hear the voice that is crying to be heard: the voice belonging to Don Smith.

I owned a hardware store for many years; and I was always at work by 7 a.m. to set up the workstations, sweep, and make sure the trash was placed on the curb for sanitation to take.

Next door to my hardware store is a coffee shop that makes the best lattes in all of the Bronx. I always loved my coffee and my bran muffins. Every morning, like clockwork, I arrived at the coffee shop at 6:30 a.m. and had a muffin and my favorite blend for the day. But, today was inventory Friday, and my assistant and I were supposed to be at the shop at 5 a.m. to take inventory on the boxes delivered the night before. As I arrived, a black sedan pulled up in front of the store. Thinking it was Ted, my assistant, I opened the shop and left the door unlocked behind me as I normally do.

I never saw who came into the store that morning. I had my back to the register, and I was bending over some boxes, grabbing the keys, fuses, and hammers that I had ordered. Checking things off of the master list, the next thing I knew I was out cold.

Something sharp and hard had hit me over the head. The lights definitely went out — but not before I smelled the person's cologne and, recognizing it, realized who hit me; but it was too late. Why would this person want me out of the way?

I am now six feet underground behind this stone that has turned green with mold, with no one coming to see me except a lone driver. Hear my voice as I tell you my story, and maybe you will visit me, and I won't be that lonely person behind that last stone in the cemetery.

My name is Don and, as you know, I was the manager and owner of Hardware City. On the weekends my wife, Eugenia, and my daughter, Maria, always helped out in the store, when we were the busiest. Ted, my assistant, was quite helpful, but lately he had been calling in sick or coming in late; in general, he was becoming much less dependable.

Last week, something strange happened. An unknown number called the store every day at the same time with the same message: "I know who you really are, and I know what you did."

The voice would repeat this message over and over, until I stopped answering them. I was frightened, so I called the police and played a recording of it for them. They did nothing.

That Wednesday, as I arrived after getting my coffee and muffin at the shop next door, I saw the front door covered in red paint with the following message:

You are going to die!
You deserve whatever I do to you!
Signed,
Your fate

My hands began to shake. The coffee dropped on the sidewalk. I barely made it inside. I tried dialing 911 but the landline was cut. Using my cell phone, I managed to call 911 and then my wife. I was having trouble breathing, and my blood pressure must have shot up way above normal.

When the police arrived, I explained everything, showing them the front door ... but they just stared at me in disbelief.

"There is nothing on your front door, Don," one officer said. "You must be seeing things. And when we traced the calls on your phone, the only ones that were listed were customers and your family. The unknown caller must have been another figment of your imagination."

The officer told me not to bother them again, as my wife stood behind me with a strange look on her face. Something weird was happening. I am not one to make things up or imagine things. How could the paint disappear from the front door? Who could have cleaned it up? Who wanted me out of the way and what part did my wife have in all of this?

I sent my wife and daughter home and told them to call me when they arrived, but I never heard from them. I tried calling my wife and got her answering machine on both her cell phone and our home phone.

Trying to shake off the events of the day, I opened the store and dealt with all of the customers by myself since my assistant called in sick once again. At five, I left for home. I could sense that someone was following me. I was uneasy, to say the least.

When I arrived home, Eugenia was making dinner, and I asked her why she never called me when she got home. She claimed she did and got my voicemail — I knew that was not true. However, thinking that maybe I was working too hard or just imagining things, I decided to put the entire incident aside. But I now know that I should not have.

You may be wondering: what could I have done to warrant this treatment? Well, as a teenager, I did some things I am not proud of. Of course, I never hurt or hit anyone or stole anything. But I was not very nice to some other kids at my school, and I would pick on them and call them nasty names. I even tripped the nerdy kids during gym class.

I remember one incident in particular. Morris, a fellow student, was walking into the gym one morning with his friend Sam. Both of them, believe it or not, were six feet tall and weighed over two-hundred pounds each — at sixteen years old. They were mean and always played dirty tricks on the other kids. I was not much better, but what they did could have could seriously injured someone, or worse.

Morris and Sam approached me and made me an offer that I could not refuse. They knew it was me who had locked Stan in his locker for an hour because he ratted me out to the gym teacher; they knew that I was the one who put grease all over the captain of the football team's sneakers because he stole my girlfriend; they knew even more than I care to admit. So, they explained what they wanted done, and that if I did not go along with their plan, they would rat on me and ensure that I paid for all of my misdeeds. I do want to tell you what I did; but someone did get hurt, and the end was not pretty.

So, looking into my past, it had become clear how I ended up in danger: someone found out about what I did back then and threatened to tell. But it could not have been Morris or Sam because they were both in jail.

Fast forward a little, and here I am in the hospital in serious condition, with a head injury that the doctors say will make a vegetable for the rest of my life — if I make it at all. But even though I am on life support, I am able to hear everything being said. My wife does not seem to be upset, and my daughter never comes to see me. Ted has taken over the store and even wants to buy me out. Eugenia knew about my past because I told her everything before we were married, over twenty years ago.

Eugenia is forty-six and is quite stunning. I am fifty and have always been in good shape for a man my age. Lately, though, Eugenia has been hitting the gym more often and going out with her single friends two or three nights a week…

The doctor just came into the room and told her that the weapon the police found at the scene was a hammer. There was no sign of forced entry and no footprints, and the hammer was wiped clean. My surveillance cameras were knocked out, and the tapes were missing. The police did not really seem concerned about my condition, nor did they actually think they would find the person who did this to me. But I knew who it was, and now I had to find a way to communicate with someone I trusted to pay this person back.

Every near-death experience has a short-lived silver lining; well, not really, but let's just say that somehow a brief miracle has occurred: someone just walked into the room with the medical staff, who is about to remove my life support.

For one brief moment, I open my eyes and stare into the face of my killer. For one brief moment, I am able to lift my hand and point a finger at this person. That is all I can do, but it is enough.

As the nurse is about to put another IV in my arm and shoot me up with morphine to hasten my demise, I do something no one expects. I might be the last face behind the stone but in the next row of stones, one of them belongs to … You figure it out.

Who wanted me out of the way to collect the insurance money? Who wanted me out of the way so no one would know what he had done in the past?

Morris and Sam might have blackmailed me, but I knew something about someone that was much worse. I never blackmailed this person, and I would never give them up. The evidence was in a safety deposit box in my bank, to be opened in case I died or something unexpected happened to me. My banker had the only other key.

Why wouldn't the police follow up on the threat and the red paint? Why wouldn't the police trace the phone calls and learn who the caller was? They never did anything to find out, and they never would.

Officer Jones: *Good Night!*

Epilogue

Sometimes, your past becomes your present, and the things you want others never to learn about you are uncovered. Officer Jones was not who he said he was; he was really a hit man for Morris and Sam, sent to make sure that I was silenced.

Rosie's Words: I Did Survive!

As I lay here in my coffin, I wanted to tell my story in my own words, before I can no longer speak.

My name is Rosie, and my parents were Bella and Joseph. One morning, my life became a nightmare when my sisters and I went out to do some chores for our parents. Walking to the local market to get the necessary ingredients that my mom needed to bake some bread, we were accosted by men, placed in a truck, and covered with tarp. No one saw us, as the streets were quiet that early in the morning, and we were too terrified to scream.

I had always been happy all my life, and my sisters and I loved being together. We got along, except for the usual sisterly arguments about borrowing clothes or shoes or dating boys.

But on that warm and sunny morning, a black cloud would shroud all of us. The fear that was in our hearts could be seen on each of our faces. Never had we expected what happened or what would become of our lives at that moment.

Underneath the tarp, the men taped our mouths and placed something over our heads to blind us. I counted the minutes in my head as I feared for our lives.

When the truck came to a halt, we were dragged out, thrown on the dirty ground, and warned not to move an inch. When we were finally allowed to see the light, we were standing in front of a gate marked with a name I won't even utter.

Separated from my sisters and placed in a cold, muddy cell, with nothing more than a small cot, a flimsy dress, and dirty water, and with no air or ventilation, I sat down in the corner of the room and cried — alone, fearful, and not knowing why I was there. I sat by the bolted-shut door, listening, trying to understand what my captors wanted from me and my sisters. I had no idea if they were alive or dead.

That was just the beginning of my nightmare, one that lasted for months — or maybe even years, for I lost track of the time.

I was placed in a filthy cell, with rodents crawling from every hole in every corner. There were no windows, no vents, just a small metal opening in the door to push food through — food that I would rarely touch because, smelling it, I could tell it was drugged and would make me even sicker than I already was.

My cot had a small mattress and pillow, and a blanket with holes in it. The cell was about four feet long and six feet wide. The bars on the door were so close together that I could barely see outside, but the screams and cries of the others could not be ignored. Fear entered my heart, and I had no idea what they were going to do to me or why.

Doctors are supposed to save lives, not destroy them.

It was the period of the Third Reich, and those Nazi doctors violated more than my privacy and dignity — they tore at my inner core and soul. They were cruel, relentless, and heartless, and demanded total submission. They taunted us every chance they got, and the tortures were many.

One morning, after trying to force me to eat "oatmeal" (instead it resembled someone's stomach contents), they took me into a stark white lab and placed a burning hot sun lamp on my lower parts. They did that many times, and the pain was horrific. My screams were unheard, and the faces of those observing me were frightening: they just smiled, laughed, and wrote down what they saw.

For those who were cremated, it only took about twenty minutes for them to die; they were taken into the crematorium and burned, and then their ashes were thrown into a coffin. Any bones or residue was just thrown on the ground. Those that survived lived with their torment for years to come and had many sleepless nights.

***

Remarkably, there were instances of both individual and collective efforts to fight back inside of Auschwitz. Poles, Communists, and other national groups established networks inside the main camp. A few Jews escaped from Birkenau, and there were recorded assaults on Nazi guards, even at the entrance to the gas chambers.

The "Sonderkommando Revolt," in October 1944, is an extraordinary example of physical resistance. Of those who received numbers at Auschwitz-Birkenau, only 65,000 survived. It is estimated that only about 200,000 people who passed through all of the Auschwitz camps survived. Historians and analysts estimate that the number of people murdered at Auschwitz was somewhere between 2.1 million and 4 million, of whom the vast majority were Jews. Unfortunately, their prisoner numbers were burned into their arms; many hid them when this was over, not wanting the world to know what they had endured.

***

Every day was worse than the one before, and I feared I would soon be one of those thrown into the burning inferno, and then into a hole with the rest of the bodies. They were heartless and frightening, these less-than-human captors, and my heart palpitations came more frequently. It took every ounce of thought and energy to calm myself down.

I endured many indignities, and so many horrific moments, lying exposed on a table, held with restraints, the cold metal like ice attached to my bare skin. The men who performed these experiments, and the nurses that accompanied them, were cruel and sadistic, and their evil countenances resonated. They flaunted their air of superiority, ridding the world of what they claimed were inferior classes and women who might give birth to children greater than their own.

Fear was in my heart as they stared at me, and I prayed that they would forget that I was even there, as their cold stares caused chills to run down my spine. I lived each day not knowing if I'd make the next. My skin browned, my eyes became sallow, and my body looked skeletal, as I prayed each day for an end to my misery.

One night, when I was back in my barracks with so many others, I heard voices outside and wondered what they had planned. They thought we could not hear them — or that we were asleep on the cold floors that were our beds, with nothing to cover us but some old smelly sheets or blankets — but from what I heard, they believed the Allies were coming, and so all of us might be sent to our deaths before our captors fled.

What happened after that is only what I can recall — but it may have happened another way, so please don't hold me to my account.

Several men came into our barracks, covered us with warm blankets, and gave us water to drink, and gestured that we stay quiet. Not moving a muscle and not knowing who they were, or if we could trust them, I prayed that I would make it out and never have to return. My sisters were somewhere, but I had no idea where.

Someone else was in the room, hidden by a hat covering his head, just letting his deep blue eyes shine through; I realized I knew him. "Max," I whispered. He gestured, letting me know that he was there to rescue us.

The next thing I knew, I was outside with the others, going into an underground tunnel, hoping that at the other end I would see sunshine. The tunnel was dark and dank, and smelled of dead animals and rot, but at the moment, it was like a palace bringing me to freedom.

When we finally came to the end of the tunnel, we were led inside a truck, covered over by tarp so no one would see us, and driven to a house, where a family lived who would care for us until we could be moved once again. The family might have been Germans, and they did not say much at all, but they cared for us and gave us food and clothing. For the first time, I felt safe; but for how long?

Unfortunately, not everything went smoothly after that: someone came to the house where we were hiding and tried to enter and search for prisoners that might have escaped from the camp.

Fanny and I searched for somewhere to hide. (Fanny is my grandmother; later, I found out she is actually my grandmother's sister. I learned this after my grandmother's death.)

We found an opening in the floor that led to a hidden cellar and prayed that we would be able to climb down, quietly, and not be found out; if we were discovered, not only would our lives end but also the lives of the family that was hiding us. We hoped that no one would hear us, and that Max would eventually return.

With little air, just enough water for about two or three days, and a limited amount of food stored in the cellar, we were ready to give up when someone came down the ladder. We did not reveal ourselves but hoped it was Max; and whispering our names, Max appeared as promised. But the road to freedom still had many obstacles, and we had to find a way to leave the house unseen.

In the dead of the night, with freezing temperatures and the snow coming down, wearing whatever the family could find to keep us warm, we entered what was to be our passage to freedom: an underground tunnel. As we entered the tunnel, we heard a group of men speaking — we did not learn their names, but their goal was to get us to safety somehow.

Days passed — weeks — and then, finally, as we traveled in darkness to Switzerland, a glimmer of light appeared once again: Max, our savior. With his help and the help of so many more people whose faces were all a blur, I wound up on Ellis Island in America. Where would I go from there? What would my destiny be? I didn't care. I just knew that I was finally safe from those monsters.

But now I had to learn my real fate. I often asked myself, What had they done to me? How would the x-rays and all that they did to me change my life by making her sterile and not able to have my own children. How could I ever forget the horrors I experienced?

Leaving those horrors behind wasn't the end; there would be new ones. When I entered Ellis Island, I prayed for my safety and my sanity. The pain inflicted on me and so many others could not be denied; no one would ever be able to really understand my fear of the dark or being alone. I even feared going to the doctor's office: when I accidentally burned my hand (after the grease spattered while cooking), I refused to go to the doctor. The doctor's metal table and the medical instruments brought back such bad memories that I told my family to instead bring me something from the pharmacy to heal my burn.

I still trembled when anyone came close to me. I often had nightmares about what was done to me. Though I was safe, I never really felt safe. I hoped to be reunited with my sisters and Max — who continued to play an important role in my life. I was convinced, by Max and others, that I needed some medical attention due to the physical and mental abuse I had received.

My physical condition was poor when I arrived to the United States, and I needed to go through many medical tests and exams just to find out how the Nazis' treatment of me would affect me in the future. I remembered some of the tortures — others I chose to forget. Every day, I found myself dealing with stomach problems, headaches, and pain all over my body; real or imagined, I didn't know. At times, I saw myself on that cold metal table, saw the horrific faces of those monsters, and heard the screams of so many about to be slaughtered.

Going through Ellis Island has become a blur in my mind. All I remember is hoping I would be allowed to enter America. I had a constant fear that they would send me back. Learning to trust my new country would take time and patience on the part of so many people. Would I ever really be free? What would my freedom be like in this new world?

To become more familiar with my new surroundings, I tried to walk long distances, which was hard; my blurred eyes could not see clearly. Later, I learned I had cataracts, but I still didn't understand how or why I'd gotten them.

Long nights and hard days passed before I felt safe even walking on the streets. But my eyes were so bad that in order to get anywhere, I needed someone with me, or I had to count my steps wherever I went, hoping to reach my destination without having to cross many streets. I could not see the colors of the streetlights, but I knew which one was green by its location on the lamp; or I would ask someone to help me cross.

Fanny and Max found each other and married months after our escape. Things were great for quite some time, and they had five beautiful children to care for, nurture, and love. I was an aunt. But life brought other hardships and strife.

When Fanny was about to give birth to child number six, she developed pneumonia, and she and the baby died in childbirth, leaving Max alone with five children aged two to twelve. I wondered how he would handle it. How would he continue to support his family without a wife to care for them?

Max struggled for a long time, until he made a life-changing choice. As he had to work, he needed someone to care for his children, and that meant taking a new wife. Shondina, Tillie, or I were the logical options, as we were the aunts of his five children. After getting to know each one of us more, he realized that I would be a perfect fit; but would his children accept me? Becoming his wife would be fine but understanding and fulfilling my duties as a wife would take time.

I still woke up in the middle of the night and thought I was back in that room, on that metal cot, with those evil eyes staring at me. I would yell and scream, believing I would never be the same, even with my family and my husband, Max, helping and guiding me every single day. His children did not really accept me as their parent after their real mother passed away in childbirth, but their father needed someone to step in and take care of them.

Life had not been easy for me, and at times, I felt that I had been trapped in another type of prison since coming to America. I loved being with Max and his family, but the children still had a long way to go to realize that I was not trying to take the place of their mother. I was just hoping to be a part of their lives.

I might be gone, telling you this story from behind a stone in a cemetery, but I hope to show people that these events really did happen, and that no one will never forget. I'm not sure if I was ever free. For my whole life, married to Max, I was blessed, and his — or our — children were the biggest blessings in my life. But things never really went smoothly, and freedom was something I never felt again.

When I passed away, Max found a red case with a lock on it, which I had carried with me wherever I went. It was under my bed, and no one ever knew what was in it or why I was so protective of the contents. When Max opened it after my passing, there was a note in it, asking that one of my children (which one I will not say) write my story for me, as I could not read or write. The note also stated what was in the box, what was to be done with it, and why I never learned to trust those that were not under my own roof. Freedom: I still don't know if I will ever be free!

Her Final Repose

Hidden beneath a stone with my eyes wide open and my body covered in a sheet, and nothing below the sheet, I was buried alive to live out my final hours in this airtight coffin. Just why this happened to me, and how, will be revealed slowly and methodically. I hope someone will hear my screams, dig deep into the ground, and save me before the bugs eat their way through my thin sheet, destroy my face, and take away my last ounce of breath.

My hands have been tied to the side of the coffin and I can't move them. My legs are bound. My mouth was taped, but I managed to get it off, somehow. Life handed me a tough deal, and my final repose is where I have wound up. I'll tell you my story, and you can decide if I belong in the ground, behind this next unmarked stone.

My name is Benita, and I was once a prostitute, pole dancer, and soap star. I managed to get along with the help of the Johns that I screwed: the men that gave me money and showed me a good time — but I showed them even more. Some were married. The director of the soap that I starred in used me for his own pleasures in order to keep me employed. If not, I would have been fired. You see, I am not a great actress, but I am a fantastic bed partner.

When I realized that I needed more out of life, I decided to take on a different job: catering and event planning. I thought I could pretend that I knew how to handle the daily events needed to run a catering hall and the employees. The catering hall was in a small town, and the owner took to my appearance in a heartbeat. Alonzo Rivera was his name, and his wife ran the office. She was overweight and had dark hair tied in a bun, thick glasses, and a hardcore attitude. When Alonzo hired me, she was very unhappy.

My job was to help plan weddings, parties, retirement parties, business meetings, and other events. I made sure that there were not more than three events daily. No one watched over what I was doing, and each type of event had its own planning sheet, prices, and costs. No one would notice if I added some zeros to some of the smaller items — the cost of flowers, music, and even invitations and place cards. I always handed in the right invoice but gave the customer the other one. And I always requested that they give me cash for these incidentals so that they would not be taxed. No one ever questioned me; at least, not until Sarah Jones came into my life.

That's when the nightmare began.

Sarah Jones was a rich bitch who had more money than she ever needed. So what if I fleeced her out of some? Sarah came from a rich family, but she had made it on her own. She was a criminal defense lawyer and was married to a doctor who had several offices all over the state. Her two sisters were not quite as well off, but she couldn't care less about them.

I found out their finances were not quite as lucrative as hers, and they were always asking her for help, but she ignored them. I found this out by prying into her life and asking questions, just to pretend to get to know her better. She felt that she worked for what she had, and so should they.

Sarah entered my office one day wearing a black, pencil-thin, straight skirt. She had on a white turtleneck and black jacket buttoned in the center. Her five-inch heels came from Nordstrom, and her handbag was from Kate Spade. She oozed money, and her personality oozed, "Don't dare go against my wishes." Her handshake was strong and her grip even stronger, and she did not smile or show any emotions.

Requesting to see the various packages for the events that she wanted to host, I showed her packages for business meetings with lunch, breakfast meetings, and late-night parties with cocktails, drinks, and music. I then explained that certain incidentals needed to be paid for in cash in order to lower the taxes, giving her a 10 percent discount on all of the packages.

She seemed suspicious at first but finally agreed; however, she insisted on a written statement of all her costs, including those that she paid for in cash. Hesitating, I told her that it would create a problem, but, in the end, I had no choice. Rather than lose the money or fear that she would tell my boss what I was doing, I added some extra orders to the party on us, and then created another invoice with the incidentals but jacked up the prices so that I would make a profit.

Signing the forms and leaving a deposit for the three events — the luncheon, the breakfast, and the nighttime event — she took home the sheet and would let me know if there was anything else she needed besides staff to run each event. She wanted to interview each one before agreeing to finalize the plans.

One day, Sarah returned to the catering hall to meet Alonzo and his wife, Carmella — who, from the start, had hated me and wanted me out of the way. I never realized that she was the brains behind the business, and that Sarah had her in her pocket all that time.

Now, Sarah Jones might have billed herself as a lawyer, but in reality, she was an undercover agent for the FBI and also worked part time for the US Treasury. She took on money laundering cases and financial crimes; and, in my case, she was looking to the mishandling of payments for the events I planned.

But that was not all.

Someone who came to book a party thought they recognized me from somewhere else and called me by another name. I felt like my face turned as pale as a ghost, and I began to shake, not knowing which way to turn. My flesh seemed clammy, and my body was ice cold.

At the time, Sarah knew about my past, but she had not revealed anything, nor had she made any attempt to hint that she knew who I really was. Signing the forms for all the events, I felt that I had to get out, and fast — I felt sick and hoped to escape quickly. Though this job was lucrative, I would have to leave it.

But just as I was about to open the door and exit, Sarah stood in my way, along with several others: seemingly law enforcement officers. However, I would learn their true calling soon enough.

They handcuffed me and put me in the back of a tinted-windowed car. I was flanked on all sides so that I could not move or attempt to get out. It was a symbol: there was no escape this time, and I would pay for all that I had done.

I had no idea what Sarah had found out or who these people really were, but I realized that someone within the catering business, namely the wife, had decided it was time to end my reign, keep me away from Alonzo, and make sure that I would disappear.

Was Alonzo's wife connected to the mob? Was she aware of who I was connected to as well? Or was I used as a pawn all the time, just to get even for something I did as a teen?

Growing up, I had nothing, and my mother left me alone at night to have some fun with her boyfriends. My father worked three jobs to keep a roof over our heads. My mother always seemed to have money, buying herself expensive clothes and shoes, and I wore the same dresses and shoes for years, never seeing anything new unless it was for my birthday.

There comes a time when you must decide, and for me, it came when I was eighteen and realized that I needed to take control of my destiny, even if it meant eliminating certain people and benefitting from their demise.

Little did I know that someone I would meet in the present had seen what I did in the past. Little did I know that I had an aunt named Rosita, and that she had a daughter named Sarah Jones from her second husband, and that Sarah saw what I did but never told on me, until now.

Sarah was just a child when it happened. Her mother told her she'd imagined what she saw. Then, after seeing proof, she said to keep it quiet, or their family might be next.

"Benita is dangerous," Rosita said. "You saw what she did to her poor mother. If she knows that you saw her cut her up, sticking a knife into her heart and then taking apart the body and putting it in a plastic bag, then throwing each piece in many different places, we could be next."

What I did not know was that fourteen-year-old Sarah had a phone in her hand and recorded the entire crime, hoping to show it to the police one day. Recording it was just the beginning; facing her now, in the present, would be the end … or would it?

My body confined to the car, I was struggling to figure a way out of my situation. But, before I could do anything, I made it to the end of the journey, at the cemetery.

The gravediggers had already dug my final resting place, where I would spend eternity. But not until Sarah had her moment. A few people were with her, and Sarah showed them the videos of what I'd done to my mother, my affairs, the money — she recorded everything. And now they all knew that I'd stolen and more, taking away the lives of so many.

I was taken from the car, placed in the coffin with just a sheet over me and a small pillow for my head, my hands bound across my chest, my eyes wide open. My legs were bound, and they tossed me in and closed the lid, sealing it.

I am behind the next stone covered in moss, surrounded by the brown and decaying grounds that have not been cared for in years. This cemetery is old, and those buried here have been long forgotten for the deeds that they inflicted on others.

My eyes are starting to close as I begin to feel bugs crawl around them, and I am trying to blink but cannot. My head feels heavy. I have been down here for several days. I've managed to stay alive because, even though my hands are bound, I am able to maneuver my head and drink the water they left for me — only enough to survive about a week. However, one of the restraints has just come off, and now I can untie the other. My legs are free, but the lid on the coffin has been nailed shut, and I am buried ten feet below the ground. No one out there can hear my cries.

I can feel the black air all around me, the darkness within my body and soul. The graveyard is quiet, and even though I am ten feet below the ground, I feel that someone is watching me.

And then I hear a shrill cry above me. Is it another victim being placed in this solitary cemetery? There are no ghosts here but something strange is happening.

I hear something above me.

Oh my god.

It's a bulldozer, and they are about to level the cemetery — anyone buried will be crushed in the process. I hear drilling and banging. I am fighting urge to cry, and I know it's a matter of minutes before I will feel the heat as the flames engulf what is left of the coffins. I heard they will burn them all, leaving no evidence that anyone has even been buried here. It will be like I never existed.

The drilling and banging continue until I feel a chill of cold air on my face, as the lid of the coffin is now open. Staring down at me is a face that I will never forget, one that will haunt me in eternity forever. The face staring down at me is that of the one person that I thought was dead, mutilated, and buried.

Whose Face?

"I wanted my face to be the last one that you ever saw before this lid is permanently closed, your body sealed within this coffin forever, then your last breath finally taken. Remember my smile. Remember my face. Rot in hell!

"Your voice will be more than silenced, and your ability to even communicate will be taken."

Someone lowers themselves into my coffin, opens my mouth, and rips out my tongue and voice box, and I slowly close my eyes for the last time, no longer with any hint of a smile. My voice is silenced forever.

Bertha

A Young Girl's Nightmare

Bertha Speaks from Her Grave About Her Memories

My name on the next stone is hard to read, as the stone is quite old. I never wanted a fanfare when I left this world, but there are many reasons why my life was hard, and why I never really enjoyed each day of my life living in America. I loved living in Russia, in Belarus with my parents. But, like many parents that needed money, they sent me to America to live with my aunt, Anna, never realizing that it would be the start my living nightmare.

The Beginning

Clouds form.
A dark mist hangs over me.

105

The sun is gone, and smiles are hard to create.
Every day I wonder what hidden truth has yet to be revealed,
hidden deep down, buried, never to come to light.

I never had a happy childhood. I rarely smiled. My parents were strict with my siblings and me. Rules were followed, and smiles and hugs were few and far between. Growing up, I always felt alone, isolated. Extremely tall for my age and overweight, yet pretty in my own way, I never expected what was about to happen, nor would I ever understand what I had done to deserve my parents' mistreatment, to deserve being sent away.

My name is Bertha. One morning, as I entered my parents' kitchen, I saw a strange man sitting next to my family at the table. There were documents spread out — what looked like legal papers — which the man and my mother were signing. They stopped talking when I entered the room, and the man got up to grab a cup of coffee and something to eat.

Sitting down next to my sister and my mother, I realized from their quiet stares that something was about to happen, though I did not know what. The man sitting at the table told me to go to my room and pack my clothes into a small suitcase, and to be ready to leave within the hour.

I hardly moved. My mother just bowed her head. My father quickly grabbed me by the arms, shoving me into my room, demanding that I do what the man said. Trying to ask what I had done was useless. Eventually, though, my parents responded to my questions, saying that I would find a better life in a new world, and that good things would happen to me. I would be blessed, and so would my family.

My sister, Bella, just hung her head because she wanted to be the one they sent; but, for some reason, they wanted her to stay home. The man who had come told my family they would be able to still keep Bella if I went to America. I begged them to send my sister instead, but they did not listen or care. Later, I would find out that she never made it out of Belarus, and I never saw or heard from her again.

After living through what I am about tell, I often reflect on the way she pleaded with my parents to send her to America.

I am not sure now just how many other sisters and brothers I had, but from what I learned later, four came to the US. My sister Bella never made it to America. She was kept a prisoner, you might say, in Belarus.

The year was 1913, and I was fourteen years old. Leaving my home with nothing more than a suitcase filled with clothes, a little money, and a strange man who was certainly not kind, I was taken to a boat called the *New Amsterdam*. My parents had paid for passage on the boat, but the lies they told me about what my life and future held would haunt me forever.

After being placed on the boat — all alone — I was told that I would be traveling to someplace called America, and that at the end of the journey, someone would be there to meet me.

The man left me in a room all alone with five other strange and scared young girls, saying he would find me when we arrived.

The trip took weeks, and the waters were often rough. Many of the passengers got sick. Cramped quarters, foul smells, and nowhere to wash up — it was a miracle that I survived. The journey was long and hard. I got so sick I could hardly breathe at times: from the close quarters to the lack of sunshine to the hot, stuffy room.

The windows in the cabin (I guess it was called) were darkened, and we were not allowed on the deck for more than one or two hours a day — our only time for fresh air. The food was awful, but at least we had water. So, I boarded the *New Amsterdam* and arrived weeks later, sick, tired, gaunt, and dehydrated.

We were taken to Ellis Island when the boat finally stopped. On arrival, I was interrogated, and my papers were checked. Arriving in America was a living nightmare. I cried and prayed that someone from my family would read my name on the paper I was holding up that said Bertha Birnbaum.

My family members arrived, but there was no hug, no warm faces. An older woman grabbed my arm, dragged me into an old car, and took me to her home. She gave me a corner of a piece of floor to clean, then placed a mat on a cot, with a thin blanket, for me to sleep on. They worked me to death until I almost collapsed. I was to be their servant; after all, I lived in their home for free and needed to pay my way. I was terrified of this aunt, so I kept to myself as much as I could and did what she asked. I cooked, cleaned, and served them day and night, and never received one kind word. It was a prison of a different kind.

Living there was worse than living on the boat. They demanded that I work as a seamstress in a factory, make all of their meals, and clean their clothes and their home as payment for living there. Most of the money I made was for my room and board, but some could be used for my own needs. I was always sad, and I seldom smiled. My aunt, Anna, and her husband, Milton, were glad I was living with them — I was their slave.

And then I met Morris, who worked at the factory where I was hired to sew. Daily, I was required to create over twenty-five dresses and ten shirts — or not get paid. I made ten cents a garment, and my aunt took most of it for herself and her family. Working in the factory was hard, but it got me out of the house and interacting with other people. But no one really spoke while we worked, and lunch was at our machines for only fifteen short minutes. Bathroom breaks required someone walking us to the restroom and making sure that we returned within three minutes.

Life was hard, and the anger within me never left. I felt cheated, and I knew that my only way out was to find someone who would take my heart and care for me.

Morris was that person.

He saw something in me that no one else did. We married. He thought I was beautiful and wined and dined me until I gave him four children.

Later, he found me boring and needed some diversions of his own. He provided for us but was gone many nights and would enter our bedroom in the early morning hours. At that time, I was caring for my two sons and my two daughters and had little time to really reflect on my life and the fact that he cared for us, but in a lukewarm way. The passion had left after my fourth child was born.

Some say that I was sweet, that I was a role model for my grandchildren; others say I was bitter, angry, and never smiled. Both assessments are true. I hated my life with my aunt. My children — Henry, David, Judy, and Lillian — were my life. But sometimes I was frustrated and needed to sound off, too.

At times, I made each of my children go to work and earn money to help pay the bills. But when Morris died at an early age, I especially needed David, or Doc as we called him, to quit college and earn money. He wanted to be a CPA, but instead earned about eighty dollars a week selling mattresses on the black market. I never questioned him, because he brought in the money. Later on, he was designated as 4F, but joined the merchant marines. Doc never graduated college, he became a dry cleaner instead — but that's the breaks.

Life was hard after losing Morris, and at an older age, after my four children were married, I made the mistake of marrying for convenience. I wound up with a man that my granddaughters felt was mean, abusive, and unfeeling. I once again became a maid, servant, cook, and bottle washer to my new husband,

Charlie, who was anything but warm. When we went to visit my children, he never smiled, never greeted them. He was always rude and distant. Too often, they just wanted him to leave.

Living with Charlie, my life became another nightmare, and my relationship with my family suffered because he did not want them in our apartment, and he would never let me visit them. However, I eventually learned how to use public transportation and managed to escape his clutches for short times, claiming that I needed to shop for food, extra milk, or other supplies, like napkins or paper towels.

In reality, one of my children met me a stop away and took me for lunch, and we tried to work out how I could leave Charlie forever. He was terrible and cruel, and although he never used his hands on me, he was abusive in his words and actions. Marrying him placed me back in another prison, and when he got sick and had to go to the hospital, it was like a vacation from hell.

We were married for several years. Doc, my youngest, took care of everything, and had made sure at one point that Charlie knew his manners and that his ways and actions had better change toward me; for a time, they did. When I felt threatened again, I demanded that Doc take me to his sister's house, where I hoped to remain far away from this tyrant. When Charlie finally passed away, I was not sad but overjoyed. His children didn't even come to his funeral, nor were they ever a part of our miserable lives.

My life was always hard. I began to resent what so many others had: a family filled with love and warmth. I guess I became hard myself, and when Lillian, Doc, Harold, and Judy all met in Lillian's house, the discussion around where I would live got heated. I did not want to go with anyone but my Lillian and her husband, George.

If I could, I would change many things in my difficult past: I would never have married Charlie, I would have tried harder with my grandchildren, and I might have even learned to smile. From the moment I set foot in America, I never experienced a day of love, happiness, or joy until I met Morris. But then the fire burned out like a candle with wax that slowly disappears, and so did my happiness forever.

Life gave me many ups and downs, but I never expected so much evil to taint the love in my heart, a love I never revealed. When I moved in with my daughter, Lily, some of my grandchildren got to know the real Bertha, while others, probably till this day, would say, "She never smiled, laughed, or made us feel loved."

I had very little to smile about all my life. Some of my grandchildren brought me joy. They took care of me for my remaining years and made me smile, and I helped make their favorite dishes. Others I never gave a chance, and they will tell you that I never smiled for them, never hugged them, never showed them any warmth, and for years to come my voice and thoughts remained silenced. I still don't smile.

The Grandmother

All my life I had to struggle and work hard for everything that I ever needed. So why not take advantage of a situation? My grandmother, Gertie, was frail and much older, needing constant care at home. Her mind was sharp, but her legs were weak. She could no longer shop for herself and going to the bank to deposit her disability checks had become a real chore. Each one of us grandchildren had a different father, and not one of us had all of the conveniences that life should have given us. So, we joined forces to get what we deserved from our grandmother.

I worked in a bar, Doreen was a maid, and Eileen collected unemployment checks every time she was fired from her job. She had worked as a waitress, receptionist, and barrister, but had difficulty getting along with women. So, naturally, when she had to serve them or deal with their appointments, she came up short.

My sisters and I had decided to take on the responsibility of Gertie's daily care. Of course, I felt, as they did, that we deserved something for our efforts. Moving into her huge house was not a problem, as she had six bedrooms, three baths, and enough closet space for everyone. The house was amazing, and the kitchen was state of the art. Taking some of what she had was not a problem — that is, until she began to realize that something was wrong.

In order to pay her bills, take her to doctors, manage transportation, get her medication, and do anything else she needed, I told her we needed access to her bank accounts, ATM cards, passwords, and anything else that would help each one of us take care of her daily financial expenses. The house was paid for, but she still had electricity and phone bills, and other incidental expenses.

But she was sharp and would not let anyone reconcile her checkbook; though she didn't suspect that we would rip her off. She asked for receipts for food, medication, and anything that we needed to get for her, but she never realized, thank heaven, that we used her ATM card to get cash and then deposited it into each of our own accounts.

For some reason, every one of her cards allowed cash advances, and we were all careful not to go over the limit or close to it. When the bills came, we told her we'd pay them from her checkbooks. We did this so that she would not realize we were taking money out via the cash advances.

For the first few weeks, everything went according to plan, until I found her will and her bequests. Everything she had — and it was millions in stocks, IRAs, and funds, along with her house, bank accounts, and personal possessions — she was leaving it all to different charities. She was still married to my grandfather, and they never had children of their own. She was his second wife. My real grandmother, Fanny, died from pneumonia and she married him. He left it all to her, and she left it all to charities. It was her way of her of giving back to others who were less fortunate.

But what about us?

My two sisters and I decided to do something about it: we went to a lawyer, hoping to declare her incompetent and not able to make any rational decisions on her own. Her medication regimen was spelled out, and we gave it to her, secretly adding some extra to her coffee. Adding more crushed up blood pressure medication to her oatmeal went unnoticed. Sometimes, she became disoriented when we decided to add other medications to her juice.

When we invited the lawyer to come to her home, he saw that she was declining and needed someone to take over power of attorney. At times, she was lucid, but at other times, simply out of it. Since my sister was an expert forger, we were able to add some addendums to the will, stating that she wanted each one of us to have something for taking care of her in her final months.

I wanted the house and the IRAs. Doreen, my older sister, wanted her car and her stocks. My younger sister, Eileen, wanted her clothes, shoes, and some money. We found a notary that notarized the new copy and it looked quite authentic, but would the lawyer notice the changes, and did he have a copy of the original one? We thought fast, and when he noticed that it was dated after the original one, I stated that I had another lawyer draw it up and had it notarized. Not sure if we were telling the truth, he wanted the name of the other lawyer; that's when we had to put Plan B into action and take care of this person before our entire plan was ruined.

***

Gertie

They thought they were so clever and that I didn't know what they were planning and had been doing — I was quite aware of what my so-called "caring" granddaughters had planned for my sudden and lucrative demise.

There were cameras all over the house, hidden in corners; they never noticed them. And I had my phones bugged so that I could listen in on conversations at any time. My cell phone was hidden away, and no one even knew that I had one. Inside the back closet in my room, I had a refrigerator that stored anything I needed to keep cold, and I had been storing away things they made for me to prove that I was being over medicated, and, even worse, poisoned by my own granddaughters. They would leave the trays, and I emptied all of the contents into containers and stored them in this refrigerator, labelling them with what they were supposed to contain — and, of course, the medications and other pills that had been added — and then made a phone call to a friend in law enforcement, asking what to do next in order to take them all down.

I had the proof, but I needed to get them to admit that they forged my signature on documents, that the lawyer they claimed wrote the new will was their cousin Todd, and that it was bogus — and then the tables would turn. *Soon!*

Everyone was convinced that I had a touch of dementia. I had them all fooled. Sure, it was easy to forget where I put my glasses or which pair of shoes to wear. I could easily forget where I put my favorite mug, or my address, or how to add simple numbers, but I was as sharp as a tack. Fortunately, my acting lessons as an adult in the small theater company were coming in handy.

Janet was about to enter my room, carrying what looked like a dish of vanilla ice cream with a treat on top. Who knew what pills she'd crushed into it? And she thought I was clueless that she was using food coloring to camouflage her deceptions.

Janet had a peanut allergy, Eileen was a diabetic, and Doreen was allergic to milk protein and shellfish. What a pity that I knew this because this information would help me take care of all three of them at the dinner party I had planned the following Saturday night.

Planning the meal would be difficult but using the proper ingredients to take care of all three of them would be easy.

Grilled chicken cooked in peanut oil: how simple is that? Nuts ground into a fine powder would not be detected, and Janet would never suspect.

Using my powdered sugar, I could create delicious muffins and donuts, and tell everyone that they were sugar-free, pretending to have bought them in a bakery that sold sugar-free baked goods and cookies. Scallops and, of course, shrimp were deadly to Doreen, but she'd never know they were in the soup, as I shredded them so finely that she'd never even realize it until it was too late. Doreen was allergic to shrimp, and what a pity that she wouldn't see it coming.

Eileen was a diabetic. Taking care of her would not be hard, as she would think the dessert was sugar free. But I packed it in, and by the time she ate several pieces of pastry, her sugar level would rise, I hoped, just enough to do the trick.

The party was going to begin at eight promptly, with the servers bringing everyone their special cocktails. The three girls were there, and I had also invited several older friends that were still around. Each place card on the meal table would direct the guests where to sit.

The first dish was a salad; everyone was safe with that. Then orders would be taken for soups, entrees, and desserts as the main event was about to begin. Each course was planned by me, Gertie, and although they still thought I was senile or had dementia, I hoped the last laugh would be mine.

The first course would be soup, and this was where things would get interesting, as I had made sure that within the soup was not only chicken stock but shrimp stock. Checking out the guests, everyone seemed to be enjoying it since I had made sure that there were pieces of celery and carrots.

Knowing my guests, I knew that only Doreen was allergic to shrimp, but I made sure that her first dish was chicken — I did not want the fun to start too early. Next, Janet ordered grilled chicken. The first piece was grilled in olive oil, but the second would be cooked in peanut oil. Finally, the dessert would be the best yet, as I had laced it with different kinds of sugar so that anyone sitting there would have a sugar rush — especially Eileen.

Now the fun began, as the next course was about to be served. The grilled chicken was up first. Watching as Janet devoured the first piece and started on the second, I could see that she was having a reaction. There was no epinephrine auto-injector to stop the attack. She had one, but it had mysteriously disappeared. She said that her eyes were bothering her, her throat was closing, and she felt awful, so I offered her some water and told her maybe she'd eaten too fast. Her nose started to run, and she began to feel itching and tingling in and around her mouth and throat. She could barely talk.

One of my guests was a doctor and thought maybe she had eaten something that went down the wrong way. Then he realized she was having a seizure, never thinking it was an allergy. So, they called 911 and took her to the ER, where they would sort it out.

But, since this group was not really concerned about Janet or what was wrong — even her sisters did not stop to comfort her — the next course would be the shrimp, and I hoped that Doreen did not react too fast. Thinking about it, I decided to hold off on this one, because it might look suspicious. Next, of course, was dessert, and that would take care of Eileen — maybe not right away, but within the next day, or more.

Doreen was disappointed in the cod fish, but I wanted to make sure that no one else had any reactions to the food or they would suspect me. But, of course, I would blame it on the chef anyways.

The hospital called and said that Janet did not make it, and that she had some kind of reaction to the food, but they did not know what it was. I made sure that all the leftover chicken was gone, and that her plate was broken into pieces and destroyed, never to be recovered. I destroyed the spoons, knives, and other utensils, hoping they would not figure it out.

Funeral arrangements would have to wait for a while, as poor Eileen checked her sugar levels and needed to go to the ER, too. I pretended not to understand how the bakery would dare to send anything but sugar-free pastries and cookies. I told everyone that I had not ordered anything other than diabetic desserts. And I pretended to be so saddened when Eileen had not even made it to the ER.

The next day, Doreen went to the freezer and pulled out what she thought was cod or catfish. She proceeded to fry it up the way she liked it. She never realized that it was shrimp because I had taken off the tails, cut them into small pieces, and deveined them. She even prepared a salad and some pasta with it.

When she took the first few bites, she felt fine; but within a few minutes, her mouth tingled and she was nauseous and had itching skin, and her throat began to close. Her throat was so tight that when she called 911 and gave her location, she could barely utter the words. So sad that no one was there to help her. They took her to the ER and tried their best, but poor Doreen did not make it. I did not know she was also allergic to peanut oil, which she'd used instead of the olive oil, since I put the peanut oil in the olive oil bottle.

Three down and all gone. What a pity!

Before each one of them went to the ER, I gave them my special smile, showing sadness for what had happened to them. Called to the hospital to say goodbye to each one of my granddaughters in private, I imparted on all three, since they were in the same place, that they never should have underestimated me, or thought that I didn't know what they were planning. Now they are finally three more silenced voices.

The darkness envelopes the next three bodies hidden behind stones quite differently from those in other cemeteries.

The surrounding area is desolate, and there are never any visitors here. On each stone is the face of the person beneath the stone as they appeared at their death. Whether they were murdered, beaten, or tortured, their faces were photographed and engraved on each stone — each one an exact, final expression of terror.

This is a cemetery that no one dares to enter, as some think those beneath the stones rise at night. Each one of these evil coffin dwellers did something so heinous, so horrendous, that their final fates belong only in this cemetery, the Gravediggers Delight.

A judge will tell the story of three grave dwellers who are here because their actions warranted a place in this horrific cemetery. Their tortured souls and bodies will rot within the confines of their coffins, which are just wooden boxes nailed shut. Their final repose and their burial were nothing more than a few gravediggers digging holes and dropping the coffins in them, covering them with sand.

***

The Con Artists

The Judge

I am Judge John Stanford Brown. For most of my life, I practiced law, until I was finally appointed to the bench. However, after marrying my wife, Denise, I learned that her father was connected to the mob and was a higher-up drug lord, which I did not know before signing the prenup and marrying someone half my age. Learning what it's like to be his son-in-law, it became apparent that when anyone on his drug team or any members of his family came into my court, I had better make sure that they did not get jail time and that bail was set.

My accountant, Morris, dealt with my taxes, books, and more. He was relatively honest until he was not. You'll hear more about him as the story unfolds.

Daniel was the final member of this group. He was our lawyer, and if you think my father-in-law is dishonest, just wait until you learn more about Daniel. This is our story: the Judge, the Accountant, and the Lawyer.

***

The Lawyer

This cemetery has us backed away in three wooden coffins, nailed shut. I can imagine you are wondering just why we are being treated as if we are undesirables, untouchables, horrific souls that will be haunted for all eternity. What could each of us have done?

It all began when Morris, the accountant for my law firm, managed to help me fudge the books so that my partners never knew why we were always in the red. My accounts were in the black but in foreign banks under an alias.

John, the judge, knew of our dealings, since Morris was also his accountant, for other enterprises that he was into. For example, when some top mob bosses were sent on trial to his courtroom, they never got any real prison time, instead getting off with a fine. John was connected to these people and took bribes, mostly because if he did not pass the right sentence, they would take down his family and some of his friends, teaching him a lesson to never cross mob bosses.

The mob boss's son was a captain in the local police force, and his uncle was the chief of police. Possession of drugs, guns, and other small weapons; money laundering; mob murders that appeared accidents; and other crimes were just a few that no one could or would be able to prove.

No one ever really knew about our connection until a reporter named Stella overheard something that would take us all down. Just why Stella was able to still walk around after that was beyond all of us, and just how she managed to infiltrate our group is what I will relate next.

Stella was a double agent who appeared to be a reporter but was the daughter of the mob boss and managed to overhear us talking about trying to disconnect ourselves from the mob and attempt to run a legitimate business. Well, not quite legit, but no longer having to pay the mob protection money, take bribes to fix cases, and, of course, do the once-in-a-while odd jobs that they required in order for us to stay afloat.

***

The Judge

This is John, the judge. Stella came to my courtroom pretending to cover the story of Antonio, a man accused of killing the butcher on our street. Of course, he claimed it was not him but someone else, but the cameras in the store showed that it was him. Somehow, when the evidence was to be presented in court by the prosecutor, the tapes disappeared from the evidence room. The notes prepared by the arresting detective were not placed in evidence, and the arresting officer went missing.

What happened next was not expected; the prosecuting attorney and the defense attorney had to decide whether to proceed with the case or set Antonio free, knowing that he did kill the butcher. Could this somehow be connected to someone on the force? Was there someone that owed Antonio a favor?

Somehow, this required a decision from me, the judge, and I realized that it would place me in an odd position if I let Antonio go. But I had to come up with a way to create some doubt in the jury's mind that this man was guilty.

Lying and cover-ups were becoming the norm in my courtroom. My connection to Antonio and his family was not known. My grandson was married to his granddaughter, making it hard for me to bring the hammer down on him. Antonio was one of the tops in this mob family, involved in murder, money laundering, drug dealing, and funneling weapons of all kinds through different channels to arms dealers throughout the world, and even to young kids on the street who wanted to make a buck selling for them.

Taking my gavel in my hand, I stated that I would allow forty-eight hours for both sides to try and get to the bottom of the missing evidence, and possibly find the missing arresting officer. Did I know where the officer was? Did I know where the evidence went?

Someone decided that they would take all of us down. Stella was dangerous: she secretly posed as a reporter for a newspaper, and was able to overhear our conversations, reporting back to the mob head. That's when things began to fall apart.

One of the jury members got sick — or at least said she was ill with stomach pains — and then collapsed in the courtroom, causing us to stop everything and call 911. She had been planted there to divert everyone's attention, pretending to be sick after purposely eating something she knew would irritate her stomach. Spice gave her heartburn, and she purposely did not take her *Nexium*. Her chest pains appeared to be real, and her heartburn was over the top, she said. But was she that much in pain? I doubted it. But she accomplished what needed to be done. I had made sure she was on the jury, and that stopped the proceedings so that I could get a handle on what I had to do next.

Court was to be adjourned until we knew what happened to this juror, and an alternate was not in the cards if I wanted the trial to turn out the right way. Hoping that no one else got sick for legitimate reasons, we adjourned for the day, and court would reconvene in the morning at nine promptly.

Things do not always turn out the way you want. Something worse was happening to this juror, something that even she did not know, and so she would not be returning any time soon. Now what was I going to do? After all, she was the foreman, and would have been able to sway the jury either to acquit the defendant or to consider a hung jury.

Both attorneys wanted this over with, but no one more than me, so I came up with an idea that I hoped would not backfire. With an alternate juror in place, who seemed attracted to me, I insisted on questioning her in my chambers. What transpired I hoped would lead the verdict in the direction that I hoped for.

But something strange happened when I went back on the bench.

My coffee cup was on my desk. I got up for ten seconds to go to the bathroom to wash my hands, and never thought that anyone would taint my coffee with something that would take me out of commission for good. As the jury was now in place and the trial resumed, I felt pains in my stomach, hot flashes, and then keeled over. The next thing I knew, I was being placed on a stretcher, and the EMT looked me straight in the eye and said this was a present from Antonio.

This might be the end of my story, but I am sure there are others that will also suffer at the hand of this man because of what he does not want revealed. My voice is silenced; let's hope more will be, too!

Lies

This stone is devoted to me because I broke some serious laws and wound up with a death sentence — only because I dared to tell the truth.

Lies are what this country — the one I was born in — was founded on. Telling the truth, the whole truth, can often hurt someone's feelings, and make them worry when it's not needed. Telling someone they look ugly or need to go on a diet, even if you're just trying to be honest, is wrong where I come from. But if someone has a fatal illness, is it better to sugarcoat it and not come clean, rather than tell the entire truth, that they have only a few months to live?

The truth is supposed to set you free, but in this case, it did not. My name is Don, and all my life I tried to always be honest, to never tell a single lie. However, the state I live in passed a law: being too truthful was sinful and being brutally honest and telling the truth was punishable. Your sentence would depend on how strong that truth was or how many people you told. This is what was decided.

When asked a question, I now had to think hard before giving a response, as there are people surrounding me everywhere who will know if I told the truth; everyone is required to wear truth detectors, which are attached to our everyday wardrobes. We also wear small little wrist bands that have chips and special sensors help the police or anyone you are near know when you have strayed from telling a lie.

Children are great at lying, and love the fact that when they fail all of their subjects in school, they can tell their parents they passed with all As or Bs. They bury the real report card and create one on their computers — since they all have the templates for the cards — and then show their parents how bright and wonderful they are. But some parents dare to question their children when they don't graduate on time. These inventive liars come up with the fact that if they stay one more year, they get college credit and can get into any school with courses under their belt. Of course, their parents believe them, and would never dare to think or say the truth: *You lied!*

Today started out as any other day at work. I am a medical assistant to doctors, and part of my job is doing X-rays. To save money, the hospitals sent me to school to learn how to read the X-rays, so that they do not need to send the X-rays to another radiologist to be read. But remember, lies are the foundation of our world, and with the new law, telling a patient the truth about their condition is illegal. However, that's not what got me in trouble.

When things started to quiet down at work, and I investigated some old cases where a diagnosis was given — and of course it was a total lie — I began wondering just how many people had died because of me and because the doctors did not tell them the truth about their conditions. Lives were at stake, but it was thought better not to upset people. So what if they think they are healthy! Who cares?! In reality, something within me felt a certain tinge of guilt, but since it was a law, and I knew that somehow, they would find out if I dared to tell the truth, I fudged my statements and made people feel better about themselves or their illnesses.

Sidney was a man of means. He was sixty-five when he came to Dr. N's office for his annual checkup. The usual blood tests were taken, and a general exam done, but when the doctor checked his blood pressure, it was off the charts. The patient saw that it said 173/90, but the doctor told him he was having trouble with the blood pressure machine and not to worry about what it registered.

Sidney was overweight and breathing with difficulty, but the doctor discounted that, too, stating that he might just be nervous. Sending him for a chest X-ray and a CATscan, the doctor could see signs of clots in his lungs, blockages, and other indications that he might need further tests. The doctor should have referred Sidney to a heart doctor for a follow up. But instead, Dr. N told him to go on a diet, lose weight, walk or join a gym, and not to worry about anything; that his tests had come back with no anomalies, nothing that stuck out as unusual. He said, "See you next year."

I began feeling more pangs of guilt but could not say anything as the doctor was in charge. When Sidney asked for a written report of his test results, I knew that this was my chance to help him even if it meant telling the truth. However, the doctor read over the report that I prepared, and I knew that I'd missed my chance since he had to sign off on it.

***

Lying is okay if it does not hurt anyone or hinder their lives. Telling a child that they play the piano well even if they do not is not that bad, since we hope it won't hurt their feelings or discourage them from trying harder. Lying is okay when you tell a child that he or she will become a singing star and you know he or she is tone deaf. But the child is only five, so no big deal.

Lying is fine when you go into a bank and claim you need a loan because you want to buy a new house for your family, but you want the money for something else.

Lying is okay when you can justify the reasons and can live with yourself after you tell the lies: You look amazing (when the person looks awful); that dress looks great on you, Mrs. Jones (it's two sizes too small, but she is smiling as she buys five more and you get the big sale).

What about the car salesman that sells you a used car that he knows has some mechanical problems? He never tells you about them because he figures by the time they become apparent, the car will be yours, and in the fine print it says once it leaves the lot, they are not responsible for anything that goes wrong.

Lies and liars are what this country is about. Politicians lie all the time and never keep their word or promises. That's how they are programmed to get ahead. Nothing really gets done, but a politician states that he is lowering taxes and providing more money for education and road repairs, while the budget is in trouble because he bought his wife and children new cars and houses.

In this new world, those that tell small truths are sentenced to ten days in a liar's boot camp to revamp their lying skills, and they are fined for their transgressions. Those that dare to tell the whole truth and nothing but the truth are subject to severe penalties, as they are tried in a court of law and sworn to tell a lie; but, of course, they don't.

Just how does the law know when someone has told the truth? When a person records their daily lies and thoughts, they will sometimes add another section in their notebook, where they write the truth, hoping no one will care to read it. They list it as "outlandish lies," but when the incidents are compared, and the logs are read by the log overseers each day — and there are many — the truth comes out. And then it's all over for them.

Lies are not so bad if they are not harmful or hateful in context. But when they harm someone or take people's lives by omission — for example, when a medical provider does not want the person to unduly worry — that is wrong. And that is the truth, I fear.

Another story, before I end my tale of pure truth: I know of a car salesman who sold a used car claiming that it had been tested and test driven for safety precautions. But it was sold in the same condition as it was when the previous owner sold it.

The result: the man who bought it was in a serious car accident a few days later because the brakes were worn. He could not stop the car and went onto the side of the road, and the entire front end was demolished, and he lost a leg and a hand. Had he known the truth, he might have thought twice before buying the car, or he might have had it tested or repaired.

Truths, when it comes to others' lives, should be told.

Truths, when it comes to hurting to someone's feelings? So what if you lie.

What do you think? Lies vs. Truths: Which would you rather hear?

***

So, what happened to me, now that I am here in a grave? You guessed it! I dared to countermand what Dr. N told Sidney by secretly preparing an unsigned report that would tell Sidney the truth about his heart problems. I also mailed copies of the report to three other people, who might be alive today, hoping they would believe what I wrote.

My voice is silenced: I was sentenced to the death penalty for trying to inform Sidney of his real diagnosis before he passed on from this world — though I was unsuccessful. His family was shocked, and believe it or not, sided with the doctor. They claimed that at least he passed peacefully, not knowing the truth and not suffering. His voice is silenced, yet I wonder what he would say if he could be heard.

There are so many voices that have been silenced. And there are many more that will follow. But for right now, you, the reader, will decide if all these people deserved their fates or if some might have been victims.

I lied and I fudged the truth, and my soul feels so lonely, and the pain that I inflicted on others by lying haunts me even in death. But maybe if I tell the truth — if I am brave or bold enough to tell it — will set my soul free so that I can live in eternity in peace.

Silent Voices: Who's Next?

What If the Impossible Could Really Happen?

Within this forest there are ten trees that will now be the hidden graves for ten people whose crimes are so heinous they don't even deserve a plain wooden coffin. Some trees are tall and filled with leaves that are brown and the greenery is fading while others are branches that have little foliage but enough to hide the bodies under each tree trunk.

Just why are these ten there in a forest called the Golden Forest of Death?

Welcome and enter as the rusted gates which surround this forest hoping it's not vandalized welcome you to hear the voices of the faces under the trees in the forest or death.

Every tree was picked for the person now buried beneath it. Some with few leaves, others with more. Each tree is quite old, and some are no longer standing tall and strong. The first tree is 6 ft high and slanted reserved for Escavardo Emillino Diaz. Each tree has a face behind the stone created just for the person whose voice you will hear.

Escavardo Emilliano Diaz: My Story

I was born to Maria and Orlando Diaz 35 years ago in Santo Domingo. My father was a day laborer and my mom a cook in a diner. They worked hard to support their family. But, even at an early age they realized that I was Ed early on they knew I was not going to follow in their paths. I wanted more out of life and when the kid in school asked about my parents, I told them they were too busy to worry about me. He is an is an emergency room doctor who does not believe in communicating with the nurses. Ordering tests and not following through with the nurses by informing them that bloods need to be labeled and X-rays need to be assessed. His manner is abrasive.

My name is Escavardo Emillino Diaz, and I could care less about what anyone thinks. I do my job but if I'm wrong and misdiagnose someone well that's the breaks when there are twenty-five patients that need my attention, and I can only give them ten minutes each. The nurses should take down why they are here, and I should not have to deal with this trivial matter.

Escavardo Emilliano Diaz is my given name, but they call me Big E for short. I'm hot and the ladies can't resist me.

Dealing with them is not easy. I schedule tests for the patients after a brief assessment and then they are supposed to follow up and label everything and send it to the correct department to be assessed.

Well, Mr. Torres needed and EKG and an Eco cardiogram and the radiologist and X-ray technician completed the tests and would send me the results as soon as they were available.

Mr. Torres became anxious while in the ER and he appeared to be having trouble breathing. I just thought he was overanxious and nervous I prescribed a sedative. Thinking he was calm and seeing him asleep, no one had asked if he had taken any medications before coming to the ER and no one realized that he was in a coma.

The medications he was given obviously were prescribed by me at a small dose and the nurse that administered the Valium gave him more than I ordered. But that should not have been a problem. Watching and monitoring his vitals I asked the nurse on duty to inform me if there was a change so I could have a few minutes with someone special if you catch my drift.

Shutting off the sound on my phone and not wanting to be disturbed I never saw the emergency text. Unfortunately, the man passed away and the resident on duty called it. Claiming to be with another patient no one realized that I was no where in sight of this man.

The bells went off the time of death noted. The on-duty nurse claims she texted me and of course I deleted the text stating she never sent it.

Later that day another patient died and then two more from overdoes of tranquilizers claiming it was my fault.

I am a great doctor but I'm not God.

The families are told about the deaths and one of the duty nurses named Sondi and a second named Nora tell the police it's my fault because I was negligent and over prescribed a sedative for each one.

The police came to investigate the deaths and I sat in an interview room in isolation for over one hour. When the detectives came to question me, I insisted on a lawyer. The hospital disavowed me and would not send anyone. Having some personal funds, I still asked for a public defender.

This guy looked like he was shell shocked and could barely speak in complete sentences but somehow, I had to work with him or spend my life behind bars. Little did I know that he was sent to defend me by someone other than the legal system and yet he passed for a lawyer. Handing me something cold to drink I began feeling odd and could hardly stay awake. I felt my body being lifted but I could not cry out for help.

The darkness enveloped my entire body as I opened my eyes and stared at my surroundings using the moonlight coming from the one window in this cold and freezing room. My body was rigid I could not move. My fingers were wrapped tightly with some kind of band. I can't feel my feet and I'm afraid to look down. I hear a sound on the stairs above me in the dark and dank basement.

Someone or something entered but I could not see anything. My eyes were covered with some type of black material and my face seemed so hot it felt scorched. The footsteps came closer and the voice I heard was like an echo that kept reverberating over and over again. How did I get here? Why would someone want me out of the way?

The voices I heard above me were of Nona and the phony lawyer who set me up. The coldness in my body and my legs were numb. Nona shot me up with something causing my throat to constrict. Hearing her words as she said her final farewell to me before I was locked away forever. "You caused us so much pain, embarrassment and hurt so many patients that died because of your negligence and uncaring patient care, we thought you deserved the same fate.

"This is what was once an operating theater and the screen facing you will show you much that might awaken your fears. The cast of characters will explain the next steps of your final before you are buried behind the first stone next to the first barren tree in the forest of death.

Can you hear his bloodcurdling screams as his final punishment comes on the screen and is enacted?

The Pharmacist

My name is MD and I'm the lead pharmacist at a major pharmacy. My staff knows I run a tight ship and each and every prescription has to be checked and signed off by me. They might fill it, but I have to make sure the dosage match's the script and the drug inside the bottle is correct and the labeling matches the dosage, the prescribed medicine and the instructions and product description is attached to the bag. Do you are wondering what can go wrong and why I'm in serious trouble with the district pharmacist and the pharmacy itself. I don't make mistakes and I'm 100% sure that what happened was caused by one of my assistants hoping to take over my job but not before making sure patients got really sick — two died and one is in a coma.

The patients were elderly and had many health issues that did get create any red flags as a result of their medications. Family members did not administer the meds to these patients because they were capable of handling it themselves. But, since they died alone in their homes, inquiries were made, and autopsies were required, but in one case due to religious reasons that did not happen.

The district manager came and questioned he staff since all three patients had just started their new meds and of course all interactions were noted and even some had to adjusted or changed.

Mr. Feld was given a muscle relaxer for pain and yet when the medical examiner checked all of his medications the bottle labeled Relefan was really potassium. The other person, an elderly woman was taking a blood thinner but when analyzed it was found to be Risperdal.

No one realized what was causing the deaths, and I know I never make errors when preparing a prescription for a patient. My assistant does fill some prescriptions, but I have to sign off and check each one. Something is off.

Someone is changing the pills after I check the prescription and placed the bottle inside of a bag, stapled and the information about the medication on the outside staples to the bag. Placing it in the tub with the others with that patient's last name initial. How could this happen?

The cameras are there and the movements of everyone are recorded but when reviewing them I saw something odd. One of my assistants returned after the pharmacy closed, but it was difficult to identify who it was. As I watched, the person searched through the bags, opened them, took out the pills and then replaced them with something else. Then they repacked it in the same bag and stapled the information about the real prescription to the front. When they were done with that, they put it back in the tub. Whose prescription was it?

I would have to go through all of filled prescriptions and recheck the pills to find out. That's going to take hours.

I reported what l learned to the manager, but he did not seem concerned. He said to just check the bin I saw on the security tape. But what about the rest? What if more were changed?

Instead, I instructed my assistants to check with me before giving anyone their orders so that I could make sure the pills were correct.

I got busy filling prescriptions over the phone, and got sidetracked. I did not realize that my instructions were not followed.

During that morning I must have filled over 50 prescriptions and answered at least 10 phone calls from patients wondering if the medication they picked up was correct because the color and size of the pills did not match the ones they had been taking previously. Some said they were afraid to take the medication and others claimed they asked the assistant checking to recheck the pills and were told the company changed the look of the pills.

This was just the beginning of what happened next.

The Last Grave: A Dark World

Walking outside and looking at my surroundings the stench, the grime and the announcing the arrival of darkness engulfed and encompassed by the overcast sky, dark clouds and night.

I'm walking through an old cemetery and the silence is deafening and it embraces and engulfs the cemetery with frigid air. Each grave has a marker but the names and dates are hidden by the mold, mildew and thick fog that embraces them. Those buried are past participants in the show and warranted their end result.

The silence is deafening and the cracks in the pavement as I walk past each grave create an eerie sound. The sky is pitch black and the inscriptions on each stone begin to radiate a glow. Talk trees, gnarled branches, decaying leaves turned into a muddy looking substance and a mildew and rotten odor that permeates throughout the cemetery.

But something is drawing me to one grave. A grave that has just been dug, the coffin is lying above the ground and the lid is opened. The stone engraved with a name. Chills come all over me. I can't stop shaking. Who is going see what's behind my mask?

The path of weeds behind my dilapidated cabin is surrounded by trees with dead branches. The howling winds, the faint scratching sounds on my windowpanes as the door creaks and blows opened in the wintry darkness. The furniture is worn, the bedroom needs painting, and the headboard is cracked making it hard to put my head back and forced to sleep on the opposite side.

Looking outside from my doorway, the clearing in the wooded area has an undergrowth of grass that looks brown and decayed.

A face forms in my mind as I think about the past. It haunts my dreams as I see him with his hollow looking eyes, his burnt skin and his gnarled hands. He's out there somewhere creating fear, terror and violence. You can hear the screams, terror of those he tortured. Closing my door and bolting it shut and shutting out the night noises as I prepare for bed and what I must do the next day.

Those graves haunt my every waking hour. Just who are those buried there but I alone will determine who gets that last grave. All that are buried in this cemetery are there because they did horrible things in life and were placed there without markers.

These are the infidels: in grave number one, an investment banker who did not invest all of the money his clients gave him. In grave number two, a corrupt judge; grave number three, an abusive husband; in grave number four, a doctor who had sex with his patients; grave number five, a bank robber; grave number six, a corrupt and unscrupulous banker; grave number seven and eight, brothers who killed their parents for their inheritance; grave number nine, a housekeeper who killed her boss in order to marry the boss's husband. Who will occupy the last grave?

The gravestones stand silently in the darkness and icy wind is blowing the dead leaves covering some of the stones. I stand out here in the cold, hear the howling wind but my mind drifts back to where it all began and how I came to be here. The darkness surrounds me, the clouds darken, and the rain pours down all over me yet I feel nothing. My mind is beginning to drift and I'm fading away to a past I hoped to forget and deeds that plague me in the present.

The air has a rancid smell and the dust from it feels dry and thick as it touches my lips. I'm standing in front of an old storefront, and I feel a cold hand on my shoulder and begin to shake and shutter. The hand had a gentle, yet firm touch and the voice and words made me shutter. "You and you alone are responsible for these deaths and why they are paying and paid for title crimes." The puff of breath on my neck and sensation that burns through my body caused a cold chill throughout me and my eyes froze, and my lips turned to ice.

Walking back to my cabin I am shivering and shaking trying to process what I'm going to do next and how I will fore fill what I've been told I have to do. Each grave is unmarked and as I stated who is in each one they deserved they're fate. Imagine living in a world like mine filled with darkness, gloom as the storm begins to rage, I realize that this world is the only one left. The population is practically nil, and these 9 people deserved their fate because of their crimes and abusing the world that had once been filled with sunshine, light, beaches, parks and trees with multiple leaves colored in the fall, snowcapped in the winter and green in the summer. Now the trees are filled with dead leaves falling, bare branches that are rotted and overgrown weeds spreading in the grassy spots that are overgrown.

No one smiles that is the few that survived the horrors that came before and now they wandered the streets until I found a place for them in a dark and depressing building with little heat, some food provisions and beds for them until I decide what's next?

This is the world most would live in as some population returns but to this grave environment. A world of gloom, darkness, dead leaves, brown grass and forest of dead trees with brown leaves and a stench that will remain. Some people have no sun, just darkness, scorching desert heat, no sun or warm air. As a result of the pandemic there are so many changes, we have to experience including not being able to at times just enjoy the sunshine without having to cover your face.

If you were the only person alive and had to live in this world I created, would you? You would experience blackness on the shoreline and the sand eroded on the beach looking darker than a brown crayon. No sun just dark clouds and no visible light. The sun is gone, and the world is hidden in a veil of darkness.

The next time you walk outside smell the fresh air, feel the sun in the sky hitting your face and giving you some warmth and watch the animals walking by and people on their way to work think about never having this experience again. Welcome to the future as you meet the man who will guide you to your new homes, explain the rules that are now in place in this dark world and what happens if you do not adhere to them or try and leave.

The cemetery is not filled yet, but it will be before long. The houses, the funeral home, the medical examiner's office all under my jurisdiction.

My name is Drake. I am the ruler, judge, and jury of this grave world.

The sun does not warm this place as the trees are so tall and the branches and leaves so plentiful and overlap each other making it hard to see past the top of the trees which are over 10 feet tall. The air is moist and smell foul making it hard to be outdoors at times. The cemetery is off limits and certain areas are too. This is a small town able to house 100 people no more and each family or groups out together will have a small log cabin, a stove, outhouses for now, no cell phones or major communication devices that were available in the past. You won't need them. Everyone will have a job and some work in order to build up this town and provide services that are needed.

Meeting the population or those that wandered in I realize most are in a daze, some so frightened they can hardly speak while some seem smug and arrogant. This group will have to deal with assimilation into this new environment, acclimating to the way of life, and learning to get along with others but this might present a situation that needs a different approach.

The population would be grouped according to age, size of family, and educational ability as well as skills. Each family would have a place to live, be required to work or assist another family with household activities that required a special skill of that person and she or he would be paid accordingly. Life would not be easy for many as each one wanted more, housing was assigned by me, Drake, work or jobs I created and expected filled after all I owned this place and could demand that an entire family be thrown out or worse if they did not adhere to my rules. My face is covered no one will ever see beneath my mask.

But this place is not what it appears to be. I run it like a prison camp you see these people are guilty of crimes. Some more serious than others and most not sure why they have been sent here.

My primary concern is hoping to learn more about these people, the gravity of their crimes and unveil and reveal any secrets they are hiding. The mask is like a safety net to protect predators from finding out who I really am, my own deep dark secrets and much more.

A sudden noise brought my thoughts to the present and my surroundings. Someone was screaming and no one seemed to move in the direction of that scream to find out who was in trouble or being attacked. Everyone seemed to drift in their own private worlds some oblivious to even their own family members and others just walking aimlessly in the darkness of this world. One of these faces will be placed behind the last stone.

The Residents

Each family that is now part of this community or town will have a place to live, given specific outerwear and tags with their names, ages and pictures.

They are all felons and have been sentenced to this place instead of a jail to serve their time. Their time is endless, and they will never be released from here ever. Before I can think of their final fates, I have to enlighten everyone about the nine that are buried and have no markers or names.

What is the real reason they are here and what would they do if they could come back and strike out at the person who is responsible for their demise so to speak? You see they are not dead but have been shoved or dropped down a hole beneath the cemetery, stuck on coffins as their only means of comfort and living off whatever I bring down to them. There are nine but one more might arrive, and then harsh truths and realities set in.

More to come!

Made in the USA
Coppell, TX
01 March 2023

13608933R00095